The Reflective Mentor

Quay Books Division, MA Healthcare Ltd, St Jude's Church, Dulwich Road, London
SE24 0PB

British Library Cataloguing-in-Publication Data
A catalogue record is available for this book

© MA Healthcare Limited 2008
Reprinted 2011
ISBN-10: 1-85642-052-3; ISBN-13: 978-1-85642-052-5

Printed by CLE Print Ltd, Media House, Burrel Road, St Ives, Cambridgeshire PE27 3LE

The Reflective Mentor

By

Tony Ghaye and Sue Lillyman

QUAY
BOOKS

A division of MA Healthcare Ltd

Note:

While the author and publishers have made every effort, as far as is possible, to confirm the information in this book complies with the latest standards of practice and legislation, the author and publishers cannot take any responsibility for any incidents arising as a result of errors. Healthcare practice and knowledge are constantly changing and developing. Practitioners are encouraged to seek help where they are not competent to carry out a procedure

Contents

We would like to thank the many staff and students who have provided us with insight and wisdom into the reflective mentoring process. They have put our ideas under pressure, helped us to see new possibilities and provided us with rich and valuable feedback. Thank you for being on the 'receiving end' of a process that has helped us define, implement and refine the role of the reflective mentor and the process of reflective mentoring.

To my friend and mentor Irma Alcazar
To all those in the reflective learning community

Introduction

This book focuses on three things: the mentor, their protégés and a process we are calling reflective mentoring. The central questions we will explore are:

- What is a reflective mentor?
- What do they do?
- What are the characteristics of a reflective conversation between mentors and their protégés that enables both to improve their practice?

This book aims to enable mentors to look appreciatively at their own work so that they are more able to make wise and ethical decisions about how to support their protégés. We suggest that it is also important for mentors to be able to show that their mentoring has improved over time. In the concluding chapter of this book we offer a number of questions that might help mentors look for evidence of improvement.

Arguably, when trying to improve practice, thinking and conversations get stuck with vocabularies of human deficit and, in doing so, fail to unlock the creative potential of those involved. *The Reflective Mentor* is an invitation to mentors to use their appreciative intelligence to focus on the best of what is currently experienced, seek out the root causes of this, then design and implement actions that amplify and sustain this success. The implications for the mentor, the protégé and the process of reflective mentoring are explored.

The core values that guide our view of a reflective mentor are essentially inclusional. By this we mean that the reflective mentor incorporates, is accepting and includes rather than puts up barriers of distinction and exclusion based upon seniority or grade. This is why we argue that the reflective mentor seeks to look for, and to appreciate, what is of value and what is worthy, in their conversations with their protégés. In this book we describe and explain how the reflective mentor needs to use their appreciative and social intelligence in their encounters with their protégés. This means that mentoring-through-conversation is not about 'good-and-bad', right-and-wrong', do's-and–don'ts. It is not about things being black-and-white, but about seeking to build (even) better future work from those positive aspects of current practice, no matter how small or insignificant the protégé may feel they are. This requires a major shift in a mentor's mindset away from mentoring being only about problem finding, problem solving and about getting rid of 'unwanted' aspects of current practice. Away from confessional tales and towards conversations about success, about understanding why particular aspects of a protégé's practice are indeed successful, and how these joyful and celebratory aspects of practice can be further amplified.

Quality in the mentoring process therefore comes from asking what is important or significant about what the protégé brings to the mentoring session. How well they are doing and also how the protégé can show others, how to build even better future practice from those things that are currently good and successful. Where appropriate, value can be added to this process if it is done in the company of others. We have developed the notion of *The Reflective Mentor* based upon the belief that reflective mentoring needs to focus on 'the positives' while appreciating the necessity to include those aspects of practice that need attention (weaknesses, limitations, etc) within this positive frame. Reflective mentoring is therefore infused with a spirit of optimism and hopefulness. To be a reflective mentor requires putting the values of inter-connectedness, reality grounded action, positive regard and relational awareness into action.

CHAPTER I

The origins and conceptions of mentoring

For many professionals within the public and private sector, especially within health, teaching, police, business, medicine and law, the term mentor and mentorship has been used for several decades. Even though there is a deluge of literature on the subject there remains confusion as to the title, what it means to practitioners and how practitioners go about doing it (Andrews and Wallis, 1999). However, even with this confusion Armstrong et al (2002) noted that many human resource departments recognise the value of informal mentoring systems and some are attempting to establish formal mentoring systems.

We commence this chapter by reviewing the historical perspective of mentoring in order to gain some understanding and thoughts behind where mentorship is said to have originated and thereby identify some characteristics often associated with the mentor role from its inception. Having reviewed its origins we can then trace its development into the practitioner's world and identify other supervisory relationships that might be the cause of some of the confusion around its title and function. These other supervisory roles that we will review include the preceptor, coordinator, facilitator, supervisor, buddy, critical friend, work based peer, coach, assessor, counsellor and supporter.

Historical perspective

It has been claimed that the origins of mentoring derived from the Greek archetype of the older mentor and younger protégé (Donovan, 1990; Caldwell and Carter, 1993). Mentor, they suggest, derived from a Greek legend and was the name of the wise old man and faithful companion (said to be the goddess of Athena in disguise) of Odysseus. Odysseus entrusted Mentor with the guardianship of his son, Thelemachus, when he went off to fight the Trojan War. The role of Mentor, in this situation, was seen as an educator to Odysseus' son through providing encouragement and guidance. In this legend the role depicted is that of the mentor being an older and wiser person and implies a father figure, teacher, role model, approachable counsellor, trusted advisor, challenger and encourager. Fager (1988) also stated that this relationship could also be seen within the Hebrew Bible in the roles of Moses with Joshua and Elijah with Elisha where both Moses and Elijah were the older and wiser mentors demonstrating many of the characteristics of their Greek counterparts. Wherever the first mentor was cited the characteristics described continue to be seen in the modern mentor described by Ridout (2006) who notes the mentor Albus Dumbledore in the *Harry Potter* series where he acts as teacher and role model to the young apprentice.

Following the Greek and biblical origins we do not see evidence in the literature of the process until the 1970s where it is recorded in the business and academic world in the US (Northcott, 2000). Armitage and Burnard (1991) suggest that this emergence was a product of the feminist movement and the development of a new entrepreneurial spirit. In the 1960s in the UK there was also a defining time with technological and political changes where people became more willing to accept direction of their superiors (Welsh and Swann, 2002) again leading the way for the mentorship process.

By the 1980s and 1990s, mainly as a result of the training of teachers and nurses becoming integrated with colleges of higher education and universities, there was a deluge of literature on the process and the role of mentorship was highlighted within national training curricula and professional body requirements. It is since the 1980s that much of the literature has acknowledged these changes and, following the review of the nursing and midwifery education, the United Kingdom Central Council (now the Nursing and Miwifery Council, NMC) published the Fitness for Practice report (UKCC 1999), which had a major impact in this area.

Changing roles of mentorship

The mentor is still depicted by many in the current literature as an older and wiser practitioner involving a guidance and supportive role of the younger protégé (Brennan and Williams, 1993; Yates et al, 1997), and it is closely related to craft apprenticeship schemes (Wilbur, 1987). Both aspects of the older and powerful mentor need to be readdressed. The older mentor has changed as students/trainees are now entering professions later in life and the mentor may be younger than their protégé. The power–dependency state noted with the biblical characters has implications for students/trainees in today's education process and can still be misinterpreted with the title of protégé where some people might feel that it depicts that of subordinate. The power dependency role has also developed as there is a more hands-on approach by the mentor and as education for many professional groups has also changed over time and there is a more adult/student centred approach to learning with the mentorship process as one of partnership rather than a power dependency.

This aspect of mentoring has also continued within the business world, and in a survey carried out by the Chartered Institute of Personnel and Development (2000) they recorded that 87% of businesses in the UK utilized mentoring.

We note that although the mentor relationship is often related to the mentor as being a trained professional and a protégé as a student/trainee, mentorship can continue throughout a professional's career and often mentors have long-term relationships with their protégés following qualification. It is interesting to note that criminals also valued the mentor as an influential individual in their lives who introduced them to the criminal milieu (Morselli et al, 2006) identifying how mentorship supports people in all walks of life.

What the literature says

As stated in the introduction there is a deluge of literature relating to the defining of the concept and determining the nature of mentoring but a lack of agreement regarding the role and functions (Andrews and Wallis, 1999). Although we note the confusion in definitions, Megginson (2000) questions the value of just one definition but supports the need to differentiate the term.

The *Fitness for Practice* document (UKCC, 1999) provided an opportunity to formally address the tutor role within healthcare and key activities that will enhance the student experience. This is supported at a wider level within the document the *Health Service for all the Talents: Developing the NHS Workforce* (DH 2000), which includes the importance of clinical learning.

Another aspect highlighted in the literature is the length of the relationship for the mentor and protégé. According to Northcott (2000) a mentor should be seen as a longer-term relationship to support the protégé and prevent burnout where there is a lack of support in their workplace. This time period is possible following qualification, however we note that in many professional training programmes it is not always possible where the student spends a relatively short period of time in a work-based placement.

In nursing, in particular, Watson (2004) notes the enhancement of the mentor's development and noted that 58% of nurses still see the role as necessary for job prospects. Mentorship offers the professional the chance to develop skills for teaching within the practice area as well as possibilities for genuine collaboration and partnership between the schools/Trusts and higher education institutes. In a study by Lopez-real and Kwan (2005) 70% of the mentors claimed that they had benefited professionally from mentoring.

Andrews and Chilton (2000) acknowledged that mentoring was complex and an important activity, however they also noted that there is little to explain how mentors are selected or prepared. They note that many mentors feel inadequate and often have learnt the role on the job.

Communication was also noted in Andrews and Wallis's (1999) conclusion of their literature review that if mentorship schemed are to be effective then there is a need for stronger communication links between mentors, practitioner teams and those responsible for education.

The main areas highlighted in the literature can be summarised as:

- There remains confusion in defining the mentorship roles
- Communication is required for the role to be effective
- There are requirements for preparation courses to become mentors
- There is a need for time for the relationship to develop
- Being a mentor increases job perspectives and can benefit the mentor.

Some models used for mentorship

Although Andrews and Wallis (1999) noted that there was a presence of models for this role, as did Andrews and Roberts (2003) who also suggested that these do not assist the mentor to carry out the role, they noted that there is a lack of consensus as to what constitutes 'appropriate support' and 'deep learning'. It was Northcott (2000) who suggested that there were two domains of help that can be given to the protégé. These include interpersonal and procedural. Interpersonal is the caring help that is given to the protégé and procedural includes the mentor having knowledge of the work situation, course activity and broader professional picture. Northcott (2000) suggests that this role is much needed for the growth and development of future generations, recruitment and retention as well as clinical governance within the health care arena.

What is mentoring?

Authors from the business sector include in their definitions that:

> '...mentoring is an attempt to transfer experience and experience from experienced individuals in an organisation to the less experienced individuals. It is often used as a king of the 'fast track' support scheme where one (relatively) senior manager oversees the activity and performance of a more junior colleague who is earmarked for rapid progression'
>
> Gregson (1994:26)

This approach still implies the age and power relationship mentioned earlier and is associated with the apprenticeship. Klasen and Clutterbuck (2002) offer us their a definition as:

> '...a process by which one person (the mentor) encourages another individual (mentee) to manage his or her own learning so that the mentee becomes self reliant in the acquisition of new knowledge, skills and abilities and develops a continuous motivation to do so'.
>
> Klasen and Clutterbuck (2002:16)

Using this definition we can see the partnership role with the protégé developing their own learning using a more reflective approach.

The NMC (2006a) note two levels of mentoring that include different aspects of the role. These include a mentor who is designated as being able to sign-off proficiency at the end of the programme and suggest these are known as 'sign-off mentors', as opposed to those mentors that may assess individual competencies as the protégé progresses through the experience. The 'sign off mentors' are professionals who have met the additional NMC criteria to sign off and are registered on a local register. They note that mentors must demonstrate their knowledge, skills and competence on an ongoing basis and be subject to a triennial review.

Mentors, according to the NMC, are responsible and accountable for organising and co-coordinating learning activities in practice, supervising students, setting and monitoring achievable learning objectives, assessing, providing evidence of students achievements, liaising with others involved with the students progression, and providing evidence for decisions made about proficiency and achievement.

We note that whilst all practitioners should have the ability to teach, not all have developed the art of facilitating learning (Canham and Bennett, 2002) and therefore might have problems achieving the above NMC recommendations.

As suggested earlier we must remember the mentor who supports their protégé throughout their career is less involved with assessment but takes on a more supportive role.

Other supportive roles

As stated earlier, Megginson (2000) questions the value of a definition for the role but agrees that there is a need to differentiate the term from other forms of support. This will help us review some of the confusion noted within the mentor role.

Both these roles of 'support' and 'supervision' attempt to improve the quality of care provision by teaching and assessing a practitioner or student in professional practice. It is difficult for the mentor to separate the two roles within practice as often the mentor is expected to provide the supportive role in guiding and teaching their protégé as well as the supervisory role when assessing their knowledge and skills.

'Support' often suggests a comfortable helping relationship where one is guided and suggests a role that is encouraging, motivating and empowering relationship between two practitioners, one usually being more experienced and senior to the one being 'supported'.

'Supervision' on the other hand tends to paint a different picture to the health care worker; this is one of control, assessment, observation, judgment and critical appraisal. It suggests a managerial position of the supervisor watching for problems and confronting the supervisee, who is usually subordinate and for whom they are responsible. Supervision is often linked to appraisal and overseeing (Ghaye and Lillyman, 2007).

Neary (1997) goes on to note specific confusion over the roles of mentor, 'assessor', 'supervisor' and 'preceptor'. We also suggest other roles that add to this confusion and include those of 'coordinator', 'facilitator', 'buddy', 'critical friend', 'work-based peer', 'coach', 'assessor', 'counsellor' and 'supporter'.

To clarify what we mean by the mentor role and the difference between these other roles we will examine each one separately.

Preceptor

Preceptors were introduced in the united Sates in the late 60's literature and associated with student nurses (Bain, 1996). It was Kramer in 1974 who noted the difficulties in the transition for newly qualified nurses and preceptorship appeared in the UK literature in the 1970s. The main thrust of its implementation for post registration nurses was through the introduction of the Post Registration and Education and Practice Project (UKCC, 1990) where it was introduced as a recommendation of good practice to employers to address issues surrounding recruitment and retention.

Here preceptorship is associated with a newly qualified practitioner who is supported by a more experienced practitioner for a set period of time (Yates et al, 1997) — in health care it is usually four to six months (UKCC, 1990). The NMC (2006b) endorsed the preceptor role where existing registrants provide support to newly qualified registrants and help them to make the transition from student to accountable practitioner.

Many authors contend that the roles of mentor and preceptor are synonymous or interchangeable. There are, according to Brennan and Williams (1993), striking similarities between the two including the assessment and role model functioning.

Differences between these two roles, other than the time frame, is that the mentor is accountable for the learner's practice in the case of a student protégé, whereas with the preceptor the newly qualified protégé is a registered practitioner and therefore holds their own accountability. Armitage and Burnard (1991) also suggest that the preceptor is more clinically based and the mentor has closer relationship with the protégé. Dibert and Goldenburg (1995) sum up the role of preceptor as primarily to share knowledge, facilitate integration of newly hired staff and obtain recognition and job satisfaction. Burke et al (1994) suggests they provide orientation, support, teaching and sharing of clinical expertise.

As with the mentoring role, the preceptor acts as role model, resource, teacher, supervisor and coach (Andrusyszyn and Maltby, 1993; Barrett and Myrick, 1998). Overall the preceptor will contribute to the personal, professional and academic developments of the protégé and improvement of patient care through better-informed nursing practice. The preceptor offers the opportunity to assist the registered nurse to stimulate new, difficult and creative methods of achieving goals (Andrusyszyn and Maltby, 1993); they help bridge the gap between theory and practice in a realistic way.

Preceptorship, as argued by Brennan and Williams (1993), has a more definitive concept and thus affords far less scope for loose interpretation by practitioners. However Bain (1996) notes some confusion between this and the American literature where they associate preceptors with pre-registration nurse. The skills noted in the US literature for this post can be transferred to the UK environment. Therefore preceptorship is an effective method of clinical teaching in which protégés can consolidate learning (Barrett and Myrick, 1998).

To summarise, the mentor tends to look after and educate and train, where as the preceptor enhances competence through role modelling.

Assessor

This describes a professional practitioner who is responsible for assessing the skills and performances of others. The Concise English Dictionary (1991) states that the assessor is a person called upon to '...*advise or judge*'. This relationship is usually between the expert practitioners who assess a novice within the practical field. The judgement is usually associated with an award, such as a course of study or financial reward. Morton-Cooper and Palmer (1993) described this role as the assessors being professionally competent practitioners who were prepared in the skills required to assess the performance of others.

As noted in the section on supervisory relationships, the mentor may have to take on this role within their practice but it is not the sole role of the mentor. Indeed the NMC (2006a) note these as the '*sign-off mentor*' and do differentiate the two roles of a mentor.

This assessor role was seen as work-based assessor in health visiting and district nursing where mentors were referred to as '*practice work teachers*' and '*field work teachers*' until 1989 when training for community practice teachers commenced.

Neary (1999) suggests that the assessor is often ill-prepared to take on this role and indeed may be the reason the NMC have introduced this different role of sign-off mentor with additional preparation.

Supervisor

This role has several aspects and role functions depending on the context in which it is used and which practitioner is being supervised and therefore will be addressed separately.

Supervision of students
This is a person who supervises the student undertaking a course of study for a fixed period of time. They assess the development of skills related to

the practitioner within a named field of practice. The role involves an expert practitioner supervising a novice in practice either within their initial training or during ongoing post registration courses. Morton-Cooper and Palmer (1993) suggest the supervisor is one who observes, assesses and practices with another to enable him/her to attain professional skills.

Sandman and Enarsson (1998), in their study of the supervision of students, found that the practitioners had difficulty in articulating the theoretical frame of their supervision. They noted that the practical aspects were easier to express and that rituals around sessions are more important than supervisor's personal paradigm. Severinsson (1998) noted the students included the benefits of supervision as:

- Creating knowledge, awareness of concepts and phenomena
- Development of a 'language of caring'
- Development of a 'model' of communication and
- Reflection gained on an effect of the intervention.

All these roles and characteristics can be seen in the mentor who supervises the student/trainee.

Managerial supervision

Here the manager is responsible for the performance of their staff and may include professional development of the subordinate. The role of supervisor is often undertaken to meet organisational and individual needs within the organisation strategy. This may include processes such as independent personal reviews, staff appraisals, profiling, etc. This is evident on the shop floor where a supervisor is responsible for the process and productivity of their staff, and within midwifery where the supervisor is responsible for the delivery of service within their organisation. Midwifery supervision has been a long-term process and is a statutory requirement as set down by the NMC (2004). However, this role in midwifery is more of a more supportive and partnership one which enables and empowers midwives (Fraser 2002).

Clinical supervision

This has been introduced more recently into the healthcare arena following the government's paper *A New NHS Modern, Dependable* (DH, 1997). Clinical supervision is aimed at the qualified nurse to expand their knowledge base, assist in the development of professional autonomy and increase self-esteem as a professional. The functions, according to Bishop (1998), are to safeguard standards of practice, develop the individual both professionally and personally, and promote excellence in health care. In this case the supervisor facilitates reflection, professional and personal development — it is how we care for others and how they care for us (Ghaye and Lillyman, 2007). The reflection is based on a clinical practice scenario discussed away from the clinical area in order to enhance care provision, reduce staff stress and provide a quality service.

Clinical supervision was introduced within the framework of Clinical Governance (DH, 1997), however many organisations have changed the title to prevent confusion of support and supervision, noted earlier, referring to it as *'practice support'*. The supervisor here may be a peer or even in some instances a subordinate to the supervisee. They do not engage in any assessment or judgment of care provision.

Facilitator/coach

The facilitator/coach are often used synonymously and was described by Morton Cooper and Palmer (1993) as a skilled practitioner who provides an understanding of the nature of professional practice through the provision of learning opportunities and a supportive intervention. This role includes an encouraging of the protégé in their work and course work issues. It is usually when a peer or supervisor 'trains' a person whilst working on a short-term project, assignment or challenging situation (Smith et al, 2001). Facilitators are those who have a commitment to ongoing education and derive their strength from their own self worth and autonomy (Armitage and Burnard, 1991).

Critical friend/buddy

The role of critical friend is used within reflective practice and clinical supervision processes (Ghaye and Lillyman, 2000). It is a supportive role where two practitioners engage in conversation to enable them to reflect on practice and reach some conclusion and/or action plan to move practice forward. The critical friend takes the role of support for the person presenting their issue and together they can debate, discuss and reach some conclusion, bringing maybe unconscious or unarticulated knowledge that we might not be aware of.

Coordinator

Again, this characteristic is found in the mentor and they are responsible for the provision of training and educational experiences within practice. The coordinator might not play a part in the assessment of the protégé but they are responsible for providing the opportunity of learning and may have a more managerial input.

Counsellor

Counselling in this situation comes under another aspect of support. The mentor may be called to use some counselling skills in listening and supporting the protégé, but counselling is not a role they take on as mentor. The role of counsellor often includes that of stress management, motivation, work relationships, performance problems and moral support. The mentor would not be qualified to provide all the advice required above but they might be the first point of contact for the protégé who is struggling and should refer and be a resource of professional services available.

Supportive roles and mentorship

All the roles identified above have a supportive element for the practitioner and their protégé, and the overall aim is to contribute to the improvement in quality care, professional practice and personal development. Each role was introduced in an attempt to improve the quality of the care given to clients in different aspects of the professionals practice from student/trainee to qualified practitioner and newly promoted practitioner.

Supportive environment

Many of the roles noted above have been introduced into practice as a result of professional or governmental initiatives. Some initiatives responded to recruitment and retention issues within a profession (UKCC, 1999), and others to the wellbeing of staff and improving client care (DH, 1997).

As many professional training programmes have moved away from the workplace into universities and colleges of higher education, the institutions have had to rely more on their professional colleagues in practice to support and assist the students with their practice development.

To be able to practice within a workplace the student is required to perform a skill or procedure and apply the relevant knowledge relating to the theory. The partnership between the workplace environment and the institution of higher education have in some ways become less interactive and student learning is located more in the work place rather than in the higher educational institutions. It is important that the environment supports this approach to development. The organisation and environment is important for the mentors who feel that they have the scope to support their protégé and are supported themselves in the role.

Mentoring within the professional groups

In many professional groups mentorship is not a registered or recorded qualification, however within higher education establishments there is an expectation to maintain a register for approved mentors. As from April 2002 this came under the business of higher education in partnership with service providers and is a requirement with the NMC (2006a,b).

Education

The government has recognised a need for schools and teachers to play a fuller and clearer part in the initial teacher training, and in 1992 teacher education for second level teachers was predominately school-based. They felt that what it meant to be a schoolteacher could only be learned in school (Hagger et al, 1995). There was a suppression of lengthy 'doctrinaire and demoralizing' training courses (Lawler, 1990) and the creation of a 'neutral' system in which teachers, rather than teacher educators, prepared students with a list of pre-defined competencies. It was the James Report in 1972 that suggested that teacher education should be '*unashamedly specialized and functional*' (James, 1972.).

These two changes in teaching education served to place mentoring at the centre of institutionally-based professional development in the UK. The new regulations for initial training in England and Wales (DES, 1989; DFE, 1992) introduced the extensive school-based component with a key role for teachers as mentors. Also induction programmes were commonly based within a single institution (Kerry and Mayes, 1995). Initial teacher education was planned and delivered through partnership and the courses developed over this time were prescribed in a series of government-defined competencies.

Healthcare

Historically the district nursing and health visiting roles claim a strong history of mentoring; they refer to this as '*practice teaching*', where mentors were known as practice work teachers and fieldwork teachers until 1989, when training for community practice teachers commenced.

In 2001 the English National Board and the Department of Health set out in their documents the requirements for the *Preparation of Mentors and teachers,* and more recently the NMC (2006a) standards to support learning and assessment in practice. In these documents they stressed the need for practice-based educators stating that this come in line with best practice.

However, the greatest impact on nurse education has been from the government in their *Making a Difference: Strengthening the Nursing and Midwifery and Health Visiting Contribution to Health and Healthcare* document (DH, 1999). The document was also considered when they compiled the *Fitness for Practice* (UKCC, 1999), which identified the resource implications for service providers and also emphasized the commitment needed to support and assess students including mentor training. In this publication attrition rates were a major problem and students stated that they left training due to lack of support and the document therefore noted the importance of a supportive learning environment. The National Audit Office (2001) noted that students were spending more time in practice and therefore it is vital to have practitioners who are willing to supervise them. These have been strengthened by the two documents that were published jointly in 2001 by the English National Board and the Department of Health: *Placements in Focus* (2001a) and *Preparation of Mentors and Teachers* (2001b).

In the 1980s, Darling (1984) pioneered mentorship in the US. Mentors were seen as being 'envisioners', providing learners with a picture of what nursing can be — a standard prodder who pushes to achieve high standards and a challenger who looks more closely at skills and decisions made. As nursing moved from task orientation to holism it reflected the nurse education move from generic to individual learning. Teaching became not just an imparting of knowledge but of identifying resources, enabling learners to gain relevant experience and offered a formative feedback outside nursing. In March 2002, the NMC changed the advisory standard in S*tandard for Preparation of Teachers of Nursing and Midwifery* (NMC, 2002) to a 'required standard'.

Industry

Mentoring has its professional origins in the world of business (Kerry and Mayers, 1995). Here we see a shift from the role of the supervisor as managerial position to a process. Many organisations have moved from the direct control of staff to the overseeing that facilitates and educates, mentors the team members and they are seen as a link from the work floor to managers. Sullivan (2000) identifies two functions of mentoring within business, and includes career orientation (where there is a focus on developing skills and knowledge) and 'psychosocial' function (where they identify 'a sense of competence, clarity of identify and effectiveness in professional role) (Sullivan, 2000). Also, Kleinman et al (2001) were very similar in their definition of the functions of the mentor in industry, with vocational, psychosocial and role modelling.

Communication

One of the main roles for the mentor is that of communication. McIntyre and Hagger (1996) sum up the role of the mentor as someone who both wears the good teacher mantle and has the interpersonal skills required as an effective manager of adults. However, they note that a good teacher does not necessarily mean they possess the skills of reflection or the ability to support/mentor other students (McIntyre and Hagger, 1996). They claim that the mentor must have good interpersonal skills of communication, as we will see later in the book where we review the conversational aspects of mentorship.

Models of mentoring

There are three types, according to Kerry and Mayes (1995). These are:

- Apprenticeship — supervised practice under guidance, working alongside an experienced practitioner (Hillgate Group, 1989)
- Competency — practical training on a list of pre-defined competencies
- Reflective practitioner — co-enquirer involves critical thinking about practice, open-minded and confronting beliefs and values.

Although these three approaches are different and can often be seen in the practice area with different mentors, there is room for the application of all three models which will result in a mentor who can support their protégé through a learning process.

The new student/trainee will welcome time to work alongside their mentor — who acts as a role model in the first instance providing the more apprenticeship model. There is also an area of competency achievements for the student who has to achieve certain competencies in order to pass a placement. However, these models should lead the mentor and protégé to the reflective model, with the mentor and protégé working together to achieve the goals they have identified. This latter model will assist the protégé not only in the current area of practice but throughout their career.

Fox et al (1992) also noted three phases of mentorship:

- Recognition and development
- Limited independence
- Termination and realignment.

This fits in with the limited timescale of the protégé who is a student/trainee.

Mentorship as a process of care

Kizilos (1990) suggested that forced coupling can fuel discontentment, anger resentment and suspicion. Brown (1990) noted that formal systems violate the true spirit of mentoring. The mentor, as stated above, is responsible for taking care of their protégé. The role is supportive and guiding the protégé over a period of time or possibly throughout their career. There must be commitment on the part of the mentor who is interested and supportive of their protégé. Also, the mentor needs to be competent in giving care, acting as a resource, guide and advisor.

Ragins and Cotton (1999) suggested that when there were informal systems the mentors reported that they provided more career development and psychosocial functions such as self-fulfilment and satisfaction from observing development of their protégé.

However, what is considered important is the loyal support of protégé by the mentor (Armstrong et al, 2002), and that they should be able to integrate theory into practice as well as encourage socialization into their new role (Jackson and Mannix, 2001). These can be summarised as:

- Taking care of protégé
- Taking responsibility
- Caring about people
- Commitment to the role and development of others
- Giving care competence
- Receiving care responsiveness.

Mentoring relationships are reciprocal

When reviewing the mentorship process, most literature relates to the benefit to the protégé and little to the mentor. However, both the mentor and their protégé can develop personally and professionally from the process.

Taking on the role may also have implications for promotion and career development, and in some instances has financial rewards.

Mentorship as a reflective learning process

Mentorship helps us learn from and about the real world of practice. This development provides better care and therefore better learning through good mentoring. This practical education is about the real world of professional practice where learning is holistic, and involves transfer, re-organisation, synthesis and evaluation of previously acquired knowledge along with the acquisition of new knowledge and skills (McAllister et al, 1997).

Learning from experience is a vital and irreplaceable component in preparing students for the reality of their professional role (Williams and Webb, 1994), and is vital for their continuing development throughout their career. Good mentoring for this can be provided through reflection-on-practice, and through reflection for improvement of practice. In this case the skill for life long learning are vital.

Dewey (1933) noted that no true growth in learning is by mere experience alone, but only by reflecting on that experience, and therefore to reflect with the student is vital to their continuing development.

The mentorship process calls for us to reflect on something that is significant to the professional, and the reflection helps us learn and develop that practice further. It provides the opportunity to reaffirm practice, celebrate success, pose questions and be creative. We will develop these ideas more in the subsequent parts of the book.

Conclusion

This chapter has introduced us to the mentorship process. When undertaking the role of mentor (although including some of the characteristics of other supervisory roles noted above) it is important that the professional is aware of the differences and the limitations of that role. Many of the characteristics of the mentor are discussed later in the book.

References

Andrews M, Chilton F (2000) Student and Mentor Perceptions of Mentoring Effectiveness. *Nurse Education Today* **20**: 555-562

Andrews M, Roberts D (2003) Supporting student nurses learning in and through clinical practice; the role of the clinical guide. *Nurse Education Today* **23**(7): 474-481

Andrews M, Wallis M (1999) Mentorship in Nursing: A Literature review. *Journal of Advanced Nursing* **29**(1): 201-207

Andrusyszyn MA, Maltby HR (1993) Building on Strengths through Preceptorships. *Nurse Education Today* **13**(4): 277-81

Armitage P, Burnard P (1991) Mentors or Preceptors? Narrowing the Theory Practice Gap. *Nurse Education Today* **11**: 225-229

Armstrong S, Allinson C, Hayes J (2002) Formal Mentoring Systems: An Examination of the Effects of Mentor/Protégé cognitive Styles on the mentoring process. *Journal of Management Studies* **39**(8): 1111-1137

Bain L (1996) Preceptorship — A review of the Literature. *Journal of Advanced Nursing* **24**: 104-107

Barrett C, Myrick F (1998) Job Satisfaction in Preceptorship and its Effects on the Clinical Performance of the Preceptee. *Journal of Advanced Nursing* **27**: 364-371

Bishop V (1998) *Clinical Supervision in Practice. Some questions, answers and guidelines.* MacMillan Press Ltd. Hampshire

Brennan A, Williams D (1993) Preceptorship: Is it a Workable Concept? *Nursing Standard* **7**(52): 34-36

Brown TL (1990) Match up with Mentor. *Industry Week*: October 18.

Burke R, McKeen C, McKenna C (1994) Benefits of Mentoring on Organizations: the Mentors Perspectives. *Journal of Managerial Psychology* **19**(3): 23-32

CaldwallB and Carter E (1993) *The return of the Mentor. Strategies for Workplace Learning.* The Falmer Press, London

Canham J, Bennett J (2002) *Mentorship in Community Nursing: Challenges and Opportunities.* Blackwell Science, Oxford

Chartered Institute of Personnel and Development Consultative document (2000) *Success through Learning: The argument for strengthening workplace learning.* CIPD London

Darling LAW (1984) What do nurses want in a Mentor? *The Journal of Nursing Administration* **Oct**: 42-44

Department of Education and Science (1989) *Initial Teacher training Approval of Courses (Circular 24/89).* HMSO, London

DH (1997) *A New NHS Modern and Dependable.* The Stationery Office. London.

DH (1999) *Making a Difference: Strengthening the Nursing, Midwifery and health Visiting Contribution to Health and Healthcare.* The Stationery Office, London

DH (2000) *A Health Service of all talents: Developing the NHS Workforce.* The Stationery Office, London

Dewey J (1933) *How we think: A Restatement of the Relation of reflective Thinking to the Educative Process.* Health and co. New York.

DFE (1992) *Initial Teacher Training (secondary Phase) Circular 9/92.* DFE. London

Dibert C, Goldenberg D (1995) Preceptors' Perceptions of beliefs, Rewards, Supports and Commitment to the Preceptor Role. *Journal of Advanced Nursing* **21**: 1141-1151

Donovan J (1990) The Concept and Role of Mentor. *Nurse Education Today* **10**: 249-298

ENB for Nursing, Midwifery and Health Visitors and Department of Health (2001a) *Placements in Focus: Guidance for Education in Practice for Health Care Professionals.* ENB/DH. London

English National Board for Nursing, Midwifery and Health Visitors and Department of Health (2001b) *Preparation of Mentors and Teachers.* ENB/DH, London

Fager JA (1988) Back to the past. Two Instances of Mentoring in the Hebrew Bible **2**(2): 34-38.

Fox VJ, Rothrock JC, Skelton M (1992) The mentoring relationship. *AORN Journal* **56**(5): 858, 860-862

Fraser J (2002) Time to Celebrate Supervision. *The Practicing Midwife* **5**(2): 13-4

Ghaye T, Lillyman S (2000) *Effective Clinical Supervision: The role of Reflection.* Quay Books, London

Ghaye T, Lillyman S (2007) *Effective Clinical Supervision: The role of Reflection.* 2nd edition. Quay Books, London

Gregson K (1994) Mentoring, Employee. *Counselling Today* **6**(4): 26-27

Hagger H, Burn K, Mcintyre D (1995) *The School Mentor Handbook Essential Skills and Strategies for working with Student Teachers.* Kogan Page ,London

Hillgate Group (1989) *Learning to Teach.* The Claridge Press, London

Jackson D, Mannix J (2001) clinical Nurses as teachers: Insights from students in their first semester of study. *Journal of clinical Nursing* **10**: 270-277

James Report (1972) *Teacher Education Training (The James Report).* HMSO, London

Kerry T, Mayes AS (1995) *Issues in Mentoring.* The OU Press, Milton Keynes

Kizilos P (1990) Take my Mentor Please. *Training* **27**(4): 49-55

Klasen N, Clutterbuck D (2002) *Implementing Mentoring Schemes: A Practical Guide to Successful Programmes.* Butterworth–Heinmann, Oxford

Kleinman G, Siegel PH, Eckstien C (2001) Mentoring and learning the care of CPA Firms'. *Learning and Organisational Development Journal* **22**(1): 22-33

Kramer M (1974) *The reality Shock. Why Nurses Leave Nursing.* Mosby, St Louise, Missouri

Lawler S (1990) *Teachers Distraught.* London Centre for Policy Studies. London

Lopez-Real F, Kwan T (2005) Mentors' Perceptions of their own Professional Development during Mentoring. *Journal of Education for Teaching* **31**(1): 15-24

Megginson D (2000) Current Issues in Mentoring. *Career Development International* **5**(4/5): 256-260

Morton-Cooper A, Palmer A (1993) *Mentoring and preceptorship.* Blackwell Scientific Publications, Oxford

Morselli C, Tremblay P, McCarthy B (2006) Mentors and Criminal Achievement. *Criminology* **44**(1): 17-43

McAllister L, Lincoln M, McLeod S, Maloney D (1997) *Facilitating Learning and Clinical Settings.* Thornes. Cheltenham

McIntyre D, Hagger H (1996) *Mentors in School. Developing the Profession of Teaching.* David Fulton Publishers, London

National Audit Office (2001) *Education and Training: The Future Professional Workforces for England.* The Stationary Office, London

Neary M (1997) Defining the role of Assessors, Mentors and Supervisors: Part 1. *Nursing Standard 11*(42): 34-39

Neary M (1999) Preparing Assessors for Continuous Assessment. *Nursing Standard* **13**(18): 41-47

Northcott N (2000) Mentorship in Nursing. *Nursing Management* **7**(3): 30-32

NMC (2002) *Standard Preparation of Teachers of Nursing and Midwifery.* NMC, London

NMC (2004) *The Midwives Rules and Standards.* NMC, London

NMC (2006a) *Standards to Support Learning and Assessment in Practice: NMC standards for mentors, practice teachers and teachers.* NMC, London

NMC (2006b) *Protecting the Public through professional standards NMC Circular 21/2006.* NMC, London

Ragins B, Cotton J (1999) Mentor Functions and outcomes: A Comparison of men and Women in formal and informal mentoring relationships. *Journal of Applied Psychology* **84**(4): 529-550

Ridout S (2006) Mentoring: guided by the light. *Magazine of Physical Therapy* **14**(1): 42-4,46-48

Sandman P, Enarsson P (1998) Strategies of clinical Nursing Supervision. A Study of Supervision models and Analysis of clinical Supervisors paradigms. *Nursing and Science and Research in Nordic Countries* **18**(4): 15-21

Severinsson EI (1998) Bridging the gap between Theory and Practice: A Supervision Programme for Nursing Students. *Journal of Advanced Nursing* **27**(6): 1269-77

Stone E (1984) *Supervision in teacher Education*. Metheun, London

Smith LS, McAllister LE, Snype-Crawford C (2001) Mentoring Benefits and Issues for Public Health Nurses. *Public Health Nursing* **18**(2): 101-107

Sullivan R (2000) Entrepreneurial Learning and Mentoring. I*nternational Journal of Entrepreneurial Behaviour and Research* **6**(3): 160-175

The Concise English Dictionary (1991) The Concise English Dictionary. New Orchard London

UKCC (1990) *PREP*. UKCC. London

UKCC (1995) *Post Registration Education and Practice*. UKCC, London

UKCC (1999) *Fitness for Practice*. UKCC, London

Watson S (2004) Mentor Preparation: Reasons for Undertaking the course and Expectations of the Candidates. *Nurse Education Today* **24**(1): 30-40

Welsh I, Swann C (2002) *Partners in Learning: A guide to support and Assessment in Nurse Education*. Radcliffe Medical Press, Oxford

Wilbur J (1987) Does Mentoring Breed Success? *Training and Development Journal* **41**(11): 38-41

Williams P, Webb C (1994) The Delphi Technique: A methodological discussion. *Journal of Advanced Nursing* **19**: 180–86

Yates D, Cunningahm J, Molye W, Wollin J (1997) Peer Mentorship in Clinical Education: Outcomes of a Pilot Programme for first Year Students. *Nurse Education Today* **17**: 508-514

CHAPTER 2

The positive core of reflective mentoring

It is 10:00am on an overcast Tuesday morning. The mentor is in her office waiting for a junior colleague (who she does not line manage), to turn up for her 'mentoring session'. Part of the mentor's duties includes mentoring up to six staff. Her organisation has recently introduced a process of staff mentoring. It is a new role for the mentor and a bit different from her previous work in clinical supervision, therefore both the mentor and her protégé are feeling their way with it. The mentor does not want the mentoring process to be perceived by her protégé as one of overseeing, controlling, or even a kind of policing process. The protégé does not want the mentor to think that she is coming along to moan, to simply pick her brains, or to just to talk about problems. The organisation has put a paper on the intranet, explaining the process. Its content is interesting! It talks about setting boundaries and ground rules. It briefly mentions confidentiality and uses the (rather problematic phrase) that 'it can be assured.' It mentions one of its purposes as helping to minimize the risk of unprofessional practice by ensuring that staff have access to high quality mentoring.

The framing of the mentoring process as part of risk management enables the organisation to go on to say that mentoring is seen as a way of enabling staff to deliver the best possible services to its patients and clients. It is a way the organisation can claim that it is striving to align performance with mission (Collins, 2006). This is a huge message. But two other views of mentoring are in the paper. One focuses on it being about professional development and personal growth. The other is about its intention to provide emotional support — for each protégé — to help them be the best they can and cope with the emotional intensity of their daily work.

Rattling around in the mentor's head are some of the things picked up on her one-day 'mentor training' course, run by her organisation. The 'big ideas' and the practical 'tips'. The mentor thinks: *Can I, or should I, be facilitative, directive, challenging or supportive? Should I guide, provide information or even give answers?*'. The mentor gulps and thinks: *'Can I do this?'*. Maybe all the mentor needs to do is be a sounding board? But would this be enough? Maybe a devil's advocate? Would this be appropriate? The mentor remembers the activities she did on active listening, building trust, staying curious and above all how to ask open questions. Then she remembers the topic of body language! She remembers the 'must do' about maintaining an open countenance and to look at the protégé when speaking. She also remembers the 'don'ts' such as, do not fiddle with papers on the desk when the protégé is talking, resist frowning and even scowling when they say or do something you might find irritating or surprising. The mentor remembers to try to present a demeanor that says: *'I'm listening, go on, tell me more'*. She remembers to try to be present in the moment.

Then there is one more thing: the mentor's office. A little panic sets in: *'Is this really the best place to meet? What about the phone? What about being interrupted? What about the protégé thinking that this is the mentor's 'turf', the place where power resides and circulates?'*. There is no time to do anything about this now. So the mentor makes sure the chairs are positioned diagonally to each other and not too close. She does not want to be over-bearing. She makes sure the protégé will not be facing the window onto the corridor so that they see everyone that is passing by. The kettle is ready. The biscuits are on the plate. Can the mentor do anything else? No. That is the best they can do.

At 10:05am the protégé arrives. Both parties practice their usual opening exchanges: *'How are you?', 'I'm fine, and how are you?', 'Quite well thank you. Please sit down. Drink?', 'Yes. A coffee would be nice. Thank you'*. And so the mentoring session begins. *'I think we have got about 45 minutes'*, the mentor says. *'Yes that is fine'*, is the reply. Both settle into their chairs and a bit of a waiting game develops. No decision has been made, in advance, over what to talk about. So who is going to make the first move? There is a little hesitancy. And then a series of 'social exchanges' ensues: *'So how is the family? I hear from Rachel that you are going to Tunisia for your holiday this year?', 'How is that new car of yours?', 'I like your hair. Makes you look very trendy!'*.

In the mentor's mind these exchanges are justifiable. They are seen as a way of connecting with the protégé, as establishing rapport and building a positive relationship. It is part of trying to use the session productively. The mentor is conscious of not leaping (instinctively) into either heroic leadership mode or reaching for their toolbox called 'helping behaviours'. But at the same time the mentor does not want the protégé to fall into the role of passive followership.

In the mind of the protégé something else is going on. She is bringing into the room a personal sense of failure over not being able to provide the kind of quality care that she used to. She has been struggling with this sense of failure for some time. She also thinks about it as a 'loss'. She feels she has lost something that she clearly feels was hers to protect. She feels she cannot do the job she became a healthcare professional to do, namely caring for patients as best she can. As the social exchanges draw to a close, the mentor perceives a shift in the protégé's attentiveness and posture. The mentor thinks: *'It is like she has wandered off somewhere, gone somewhere else. She is distracted, preoccupied.'*

The protégé's head goes down. The shoulders begin to slump. And then, in an almost inaudible voice the protégé says: *'This is hard for me to say. I feel I am no longer a good nurse. I am just an okay one'*. With gritted teeth she explains: *'I cannot do what I really want to. I am always being interrupted to answer calls, speak to managers and cannot ever complete one task well, without being called to do something else. The time I spend trying to get to know my patients as human beings is the thing I really feel I am losing. Well I have lost it! When I first qualified (in the mid 1980s) I seemed to be able to get most of my work done in the morning. Then, in the afternoon, I would have time to sit and chat to my patients, to get to know them. There just does not seem to be the time to do this any more. I just seem to be running around, multi-tasking* [said with a shrug of the shoulders]*...busy. It seems all about targets and patient flow. Well isn't it? I did not join the health service to work on a conveyor belt'*.

Some reflections on this scenario

Here is one list of (possible) reflections on what is happening in this scenario. We can always say we would like to know more, but let us try to interpret what we can, from the evidence we have. We are phrasing these reflections as 'provocative propositions', not the truth on the matter. How far do they coincide with what you are thinking?

- The protégé has seized an opportunity to speak about something that she feels is significant to her. This is a positive thing. But as she says more and more, her demeanor becomes more agitated, even angry. This might need addressing.

- The mentor is trying to resist feeling that the protégé is conveying a sense of helplessness. The protégé has waited until things are bad. Then uses the mentoring session to ask for help. The mentor is thinking: *'Is she expecting me to step in and save the day?'*.

- In using the powerful metaphor of the conveyor belt, the protégé feels that her actions (and possibly those of her colleagues) are becoming more machine-like and counter-productive. She worries that in being so busy she is going to miss something important. These are not healthy feelings. The situation is demotivating.

- The protégé could have clearly signalled her desire to try to improve the situation, to build on some of the positive aspects of her current work, no matter how small these might be, rather than signalling helplessness and frustration.

- Both the mentor and the protégé have the same challenge. It is about what to do now that the protégé has disclosed what she has. It is a 'what next' challenge. When fear or fear-of-failure is involved, when people feel they have let themselves (or others) down, when things have worked out less well than had been expected, two natural responses usually kick in. Fight or run away. All, or nothing. Fight or flight. Seize responsibility or flee from it.

- If the protégé seizes a high level of responsibility to do something about her feelings of being 'just an okay nurse' and not a 'good nurse' any more, then this sends a clear message to the mentor to take on a correspondingly lower level of responsibility in addressing this issue.

- If the protégé feels cornered, powerless and demoralized, the mentor might choose to get into rescue mode. The mentor receives messages from the protégé of the kind: '*I cannot do anything about this*', and acts to seize responsibility, so the mentor's burden begins. As the protégé gets to feel dependent on the mentor, the burden grows. The slightest signs of hesitation, reluctance or uneasiness from the protégé prompts the mentor to seize even more responsibility.

- The protégé continues her flight from responsibility. Over time she takes on the role of passive follower, more and more. In doing so she begins to hold the mentor increasingly responsible for any subsequent failures. Her failures! She holds the mentor responsible for suggesting things that have not worked out for her (the protégé) in practice, for raising expectations that things can get better but which are dashed in busy everyday clinical practice. Both parties get caught in a downward spiral. The mentor thinks that the protégé is acting passively. The protégé thinks that the mentor is being unrealistic and is giving her false hope, and that the mentor is being assertive, even aggressive, in their suggestions. The protégé responds by backing off and does not turn up to subsequent mentoring sessions. This convinces the mentor that they are indeed correct in their assessment of the protégés passivity. The mentor responds by pressing the protégé to 'turn up' and to avail herself of the mentoring process. This confirms, in the mind of the protégé, that she was right all along. That she had a 'pushy mentor', therefore regardless of whether the mentor and the protégé are right or wrong, what is in motion here is a sequence of actions and reactions that leads eventually, and inevitably, to a failed mentoring process.

Martin (2003) captures the essence of being responsible in such scenarios. When we are the over-responsible party we tend to say: '*I did everything I could, worked myself to the bone and had to struggle alone surrounded by ingrates. I've had enough. Somebody else had better step up to the plate. And for a change, I'm going to sit back and watch*' (p. 26). When we are under-responsible we tend to say: '*I put myself in the hands of the leader who brushed me and my efforts aside. I put my faith in the leader and only suffered due to his/her ineptitude. Never again! I'm going to control my own destiny*' (p. 26).

Mentoring as the 'in' thing

Mentoring activity has recently expanded with explosive speed in many fields of human service work such as healthcare, social work, policing, law (Wallace, 2001), banking (Delobbe and Vandenberghe, 2001), the military (Johnson et al, 2001) prisons (Wittenberg, 1998), performing arts (Patrick, 2002), sport (Weaver and Chelladurai, 1999), and teacher education (Sundli, 2007).

Mentoring has been related to positive career outcomes including job satisfaction and promotion (Allen et al, 2004; Underhill, 2006). For many organisations it has become the 'in' thing, therefore expectations of its impact are high. However its impact can really only be determined if we are clear about the purposes and processes of mentoring. Later we call these processes the positive core of reflective mentoring. If we are fuzzy about its purpose, then any process might do! Perhaps it is time for a reality check? As far back as 2002, Colley was asking for a 'critical analysis' of mentoring to determine its legitimacy and power (Colley, 2002). One way to legitimize and give power to mentoring is to place it securely in the context of 'situated learning', as described by Lave and Wenger (1991). This means that the learning that occurs is understood as being derived from and situated within a social context (for example in a ward, clinic, GP surgery, a client's home, a walk-in or rehabilitation centre). It is about learning that occurs through participation with significant others (for example with clinical colleagues, with multi-disciplinary team members, a service user group, with a mentor). It is learning that is co-constructed, context-related and seen to be useful.

Mentoring through conversation

During mentoring through conversation, the mentor with the protégé certainly puts the spotlight on two things. First, clarity about the purpose of the conversation. Second, the spotlight falls on the quality of the relationship between the parties — in both one-to-one and peer-group mentoring — because this affects the content and the outcomes of the conversation.

We wonder which of the statements below catches your eye? How far do you see the purposes of mentoring through conversation as being about:

- Guiding and supporting the protégé through difficult times?
- As smoothing the way?
- Enabling?
- Telling the protégé what they should do?
- Reassuring as well as directing?
- Unblocking the way to change?
- Building self-esteem and confidence?
- Empowering the protégé to act?
- Maximising the protégé's potential?
- Giving sensible advice?
- Helping the protégé to understand how things work around here?
- Promoting reflection?
- Making suggestions?
- Putting theory into practice?
- Staff development?
- Helping with retention of staff?
- Developing organisational role models?
- Avoiding any sense of isolation and 'lone working'?
- Building a supportive workplace culture?
- Improving communication between disciplines and teams?
- Helping the protégé learn from their day-to-day experience?
- To help build a greater sense of organisational purpose and mission?
- To help a protégé learn from their mistakes?

The problem with questions such as: *'What' are the purposes of refelctive mentoring?'*, or: *'What is a good reflective mentor?'*, is that we can easily get caught in the trap of endless list-making! The list can go on and on. The purposes of mentoring then becomes a bit of a dog's breakfast. We suggest that the purposes of mentoring depend upon two things: perspective and expectations. By perspective we mean making sense of things through a constructionist perspective or view. By expectation we mean an expectation that mentoring can lead to positive change. This is discussed later.

Mentoring and a constructionist perspective

'We live our lives in worlds of meaning'.

Anderson et al (2006, p. 10)

In saying this, Anderson et al (2006) are is taking a view that the worlds we build, work, play and live in, are socially constructed ones. This needs a bit of explaining. For example, what things mean is not simply thrust upon us. The meaning of what people say and do is not just 'out there' and all we have to do is grasp hold of it. This constructionist perspective suggests that we actively build (or construct) meaning ourselves. There are many things which affect this. Some of the more common things are our past experiences, our current relationships with others and our expectations. These affect what we hope to be able to say and do, now and in the future. What comes with this view is the belief that the languages we use, (such as words, graphs, maps, statistics, pictures) help us create meaning. They help us make sense of where we are, what we are doing and where we are going. A sense of what is right, safe, good and kind. If we adopt a social constructionist perspective, then it follows that different languages provide the means through which we communicate the sense we make of our worlds. The languages we have available to us, to an extent, determine our possibilities for action. The use of positive languages give us a chance of acting in the world positively. They inform our action. For example, by talking about your colleagues in a way that values, appreciates and respects them is to invite them, not only to behave in that way, but to reciprocate this 'construction' with behaviours of positive regard towards you.

Mentoring through conversation means that we build, or construct, a world of meaning, through the relationship between the mentor and the protégé. Hopefully, if the mentoring process works well, meaning is discovered, questioned and deepened.

Mentoring and making suggestions

One purpose of mentoring might be to make suggestions to your protégé about how they might positively set about addressing significant aspects of their work. What defines a suggestion? Some mentors might take on a direct approach such as: '*I suggest you have a word with...*'. Others may be more indirect, for example: '*Chatting with...might be helpful*'. Between these two extremes are many variations. For example: '*I was wondering if you might want to have a chat to...about this?*', or: '*Often staff tend to go to...to chat about this*'. This last suggestion is a kind of testimonial. Another option is in the guise of a question such as: '*What do you think about having a word with...about this?*'

Strong and Baron (2004) categorized mentor suggestions. They found that the most common were indirect suggestions. The most common of these (38%) were those that conveyed possibility. These contained words such as 'perhaps', 'maybe', 'might', 'could' or 'wonder'. An example of this would be: '*I wonder how far there was a way you could have responded differently, to what the patient said to you, to make the situation clearer for them?*'

The second group of suggestions (33%) were posed in the form of a question.

There were three variations on this. The first was a question that also included something that the protégé had not mentioned and therefore perhaps thought about. For example: '*If you feel the patient records are not up-to-date enough, why not raise this at your next team meeting?*' The second variation was a question with alternatives. For example: '*Are you going to continue to leave the ward for equipment and supplies, or can you ask someone else to get what you need?*' The third variation is where the mentor puts a suggestion to their protégé but it is clear what the mentor prefers. An example of this would be: '*If you say you feel unappreciated you could mention this to Marion (the Modern Matron) but it may be better to bring this up at your next team meeting where you can talk more generally about building a better culture of appreciation on the ward*'.

The third most common group of suggestions (15%) was in the form of a recommended idea that had been seen elsewhere, read or heard about. An example, with regard to meal times being less chaotic, would be when a mentor says: '*I know at Green Garden* [another NHS hospital] *they got one of their catering managers to follow a meal round with one of their catering staff. I'd heard that meal trolleys were being left outside the kitchen, so nurses had to deliver them to the ward. The nurses were wondering why? Also that the trolley came up without cutlery. The nurses put this on at ward level. The nurses said: "why do we do this?", the catering staff said: "Why are you doing that?" So they had a discussion about agreeing roles. Perhaps you could ask Chris* [a catering manager] *to get involved in this way?*'.

There are many ways for mentors to make suggestions that do not embarrass or disempower the protégé. Suggestions containing praise (for example: '*Yes that is a great idea; well done you have really worked hard to think this one through*', etc), and those which invite the protégé to say more (for example: '*Tell me a little bit more about what you are thinking*'), and those which monitor the protégés feelings (for example: '*How are you feeling right now about this?*'). These are all an important part of the skilfulness of mentoring through conversation. The linguistic form of the mentor's suggestions is crucial. Mentoring is not simply about giving straightforward advice. This can easily slide into 'telling' and this takes us back to the over-responsibility or under-responsibility issues mentioned earlier. However it is tricky if the protégé expects to receive direct advice and if their expectations are not being realized. If the mentor gets tied up in: '*Am I supposed to be telling or suggesting?*', they avoid telling and the protégé may avoid asking. The mentor avoids giving a direct answer, to a direct question, for fear of being seen as controlling. And so the game of cat-and-mouse goes on if we are not careful.

Making the mentoring conversation visual

One way to try to align the different expectations that the mentor and their protégés might have of the mentoring process is to make the process visible. In other words, the mentor might usefully invite the protégé to draw a small sketch/ diagram of how they see the process. An invitation might be: '*Draw the kind of mentoring conversation you are expecting*'. This drawing then forms the basis of a conversation where expectations of the process can be discussed. Another invitation might be: '*Draw a diagram of the things that help you to be the best you can be at work*'. Alternatively it might be framed as: '*Draw a diagram of the things that get in the way of you working in the way you wish*'. Figure 2.1 shows how one protégé expressed, with the help of her sketch, her response to the the invitation: '*Draw a diagram of the most important things that affect the quality of the care you give to your patients*'.

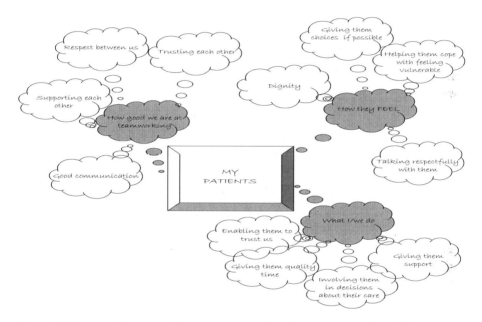

Giving them choices if possible

Respect between us

Trusting each other

Helping them cope with feeling vulnerable

Dignity

Supporting each other

How good we are at teamworking

How they FEEL

Talking respectfully with them

Good communication

MY PATIENTS

What I/we do

Enabling them to trust us

Giving them quality time

Involving them in decisions about their care

Giving them support

Figure 2.1 A protégé uses a diagram as a catalyst for a conversation with her mentor.

When the protégé discussed her drawing with her mentor, they focused a lot on trust, what trust meant in terms of her work with her colleagues and in relation to her patients. This enabled the mentor to bring up the subject of trust in a protégé and mentor relationship. One aspect of this was doing what they both said they would do. They talked about the importance of keeping and honouring agreements, such as agreeing to follow something up. They also spoke about how trust might effect what was said between them. They made a distinction between trusting each other with information and trusting each other with feelings. Finally the part of the drawing about trust helped the protégé have a conversation with her mentor about trusting them to give their honest opinion about things and trusting them to provide constructive feedback.

The use of both the visual and the verbal helped both parties to clarify the nature of their relationship and the nature of the mentoring support process. Using drawings is a way of clarifying expectations. It connects that which is visually and orally expressed with what can, and might, be actively realized. *Figure 2.1* was the catalyst for a very useful conversation between the mentor and the protégé about roles. At the outset these were perceived by the protégé as being quite asymmetrical. The drawing helped them clarify who would be asking, and who could ask questions, about reflection and self-disclosure (*'Saying what I really feel'*), sources of knowledge, about those things that could be expressed in the mentoring process and that which might be best left unsaid. These are very important issues to get sorted out, from the start.

Self-disclosure through a mentoring conversation

Self-disclosure through a mentoring conversation is about the expression of emotions, beliefs, fears, failures, hopes and successes. In a nutshell, it is about saying what you really think and feel. Wanberg et al (2007) suggest that self-disclosure is a central relationship process variable, critical to relationship development and maintenance and is fundamental to communication and information exchange. In other words, it is beneficial to high quality mentoring relationships (Ensher and Murphy, 2005). Therefore it is important to understand a little about self-disclosure and how it might link with mentoring outcomes. This is significant regardless of whether the mentor and protégé know each other or not. This is even more significant if the mentoring process is time-limited in some way (for example for 1 year only). The key issue is to reflect upon the extent to which self-disclosure affects mentoring outcomes. Reis and Shaver (1988), in their model of self-disclosure, are quite clear that it facilitates the development and maintenance of good interpersonal relationships. They argue that relationship satisfaction and liking one another are highly dependent upon levels of self-disclosure. This is supported by the work of Finkenauer et al (2004) and Sprecher and Hendrick (2004). We can therefore infer that disclosure is linked to closeness.

Why might the mentor or protégé self-disclose within this process? There are many possibilities. One might be cartharsis, another self-validation or justifying feelings, thoughts or actions. Or it might be something to do with impression formation — in other words disclosing so as to be seen, for example, as knowledgeable, important, clever, helpless, vulnerable or bullied. Another reason might be to appear to be open to the possibility of receiving or providing support to the other. More cognitively, it might be about disclosing in order to clarify one's thoughts or attitudes towards something. It might be about identity and feelings of self-worth.

Self-disclosure should not be a one-way traffic. If the protégé discloses to their mentor, the quality of the mentor's response becomes very important. For example, will the protégé feel that the mentor accepts and understands what they are disclosing? And how far does the protégé trust the mentor with their feelings in the first place (Ghaye and Lillyman, 2007; Ghaye, 2008)? What happens in a situation where the protégé may be a bit reluctant to say what they really feel in case this might come back to harm them in some way in the future?

The bottom line is how does the mentor and the protégé positively connect so that the protégé feels they are getting the most from the process. We must also be aware of the fact that not all mentors and protégés go into a mentoring process with a desire for closeness, and that this should be respected. To some, self-disclosure can be uncomfortable (Ghaye, 2007).

Mentoring and relational problems

This book is centrally about espousing the benefits of mentoring and how the reflective mentor plays a crucial part in it. However, having said this, it is important to acknowledge that mentorship relationships are susceptible to problems (Feldman, 1999; Eby and Allen, 2002). The mentoring literature contains reports of mentors experiencing acts of betrayal, protégé opportunism and having a protégé who is a poor reflection on oneself (Ragins and Scandura, 1999). Eby and McManus (2004) looked at a continuum of relational problems, from the mentor's perspective, and mapped examples of the negative experiences with their protégés onto a marginally effective, to truly dysfunctional, continuum. Marginally effective relationships are those beset by problems that make the relationship teeter on the edge between being effective and ineffective. They found that marginally effective relationships were influenced by expectations. For example, that protégés were expected to learn something from their mentor. Not surprisingly, mentors associated this with a protégé's motivation and ability to learn.

> *'Since mentors view these characteristics as desirable protégé qualities, the opposites of these dimensions (i.e. performance below expectations and unwillingness to learn)...limit the benefits that can be realized from the relationship but do not cause serious harm to the mentor or the relationship'.*
>
> *Eby and McManus (2004, p. 260).*

At the other end of the continuum are dysfunctional relationship experiences, characterized by malice or bad intent. These might include bad-mouthing the mentor to others, damaging the mentor's reputation, or casting doubt on the mentor's ability. This might harm the mentor personally or professionally.

Harassment is another example which might take sexual, gender or racial forms. Conflicts and disagreements between mentors and protégés are part of the territory of mentoring. This may be due to differences in values or a passionate commitment, from both parties, to quality care. To appreciate these differences may be a positive outcome. But this — along with disappointment, over dependence on the mentor, a relationship that seems to be stuck, maybe too intense, or requiring too much commitment — are not at the truly dysfunctional end as long as there is no bad intent toward the other person. These may be examples where the mentoring relationship simply becomes ineffective over time. It takes courage to terminate such a relationship and it does not have to bring with it any 'loss of face'.

What is interesting in the work of Eby and McManus (2004) is that creating a good mentoring relationship is not seen as the sole responsibility of the mentor. Protégés themselves may create or contribute to relational problems (as well as to its success). If relationship problems continue over time, it is likely that they will have a cumulative effect. Negativity in the form of feelings of detachment may ensue. Why should either the mentor or protégé stay in a dissatisfying relationship? Part of an answer to this is that things, other than satisfaction, may be important to think about. For example, some may stay in a mentoring relationship if they have already invested a great deal of time and energy in it. For a protégé, there may be no other mentors available. We should not forget that mentors and protégés are likely to have different relational needs.

Mentoring for positive change

We wonder what kind of mentoring relationship we would experience if what we said and did during the process were governed by these four things:

- That conversations were always seen in terms of winning and not losing any argument about the quality of care, about practice development or policy implementation (*'I think my suggestion is better than yours'*)
- That we always stayed in control of the mentoring situation despite any surprise disclosures (*'I think we should try to stick to our agenda'*)
- That we tried to avoid embarrassing ourselves at all costs (*Let's just try to discuss the facts shall we?'*)
- That we stayed rational, tried to think things through clearly and avoided getting sucked into any discussions about feelings (*'I think we should stay cool and be logical about this don't you?'*)

If mentoring were guided by these four values then we would be setting ourselves, and the process, up for failure. With regard to the first value, losing may be regarded as failure. The second value is violated if we give the protégé control of the process. With the first two failures comes a third one. We inevitably embarrass ourselves. With failure, loss of control and embarrassment, emotions are bound to surface, thus violating the fourth value of staying rational.

Those mentors who are governed by these four values do not see mentoring as a learning 'partnership'. These mentors see partnerships are something to be avoided just in case the protégé messes up and does not fulfill their promise. In this case the mentor's reputation may get tarnished. The reality is that partnership means sharing responsibility and control of the mentoring process.

An effective mentoring relationship provides an opportunity for both parties to be positive. Mentoring through conversation really needs to be a conversation of positive regard, one where positive questions precede positive action:

'When we focus on problems, this can so easily be the problem. By this, I mean that when we start to enquire into our problems, we begin to construct a world in which problems are central. They become the dominant realities that burden us every day. To ask questions about our failings is to create a world in which failing is focal. Deficit-based questions lead to deficit-based conversations, which in turn lead to deficit-based patterns of action. Yet we can flip this over and apply the same logic more positively. By asking ourselves positive questions, we may bring forth future action of far greater promise. Positive questions invite positive action'.

Ghaye (2008, p. 4)

The positive core of mentoring: its four processes

Some might argue that the positive core of mentoring is to enable the protégé to:

- Become more aware and in control of their feelings about their work and working life
- Broaden and deepen their thinking about their work and working life
- Be more able to act with their patient's best interests in mind, in particular workplaces.

How adequate do you feel this positive core is? What might be missing? What needs amplification? What are the implications for both the protégé and the mentor? In essence, this positive core spans feelings, thinking and actions in particular settings. What may be less obvious is the kind of relationship between the protégé and mentor that enables this positive core to be positively experienced! We wonder how far this requires both parties to regard each other as equals? Equal as human beings but unequal in role? How far do the protégé and the mentor need each other and in what ways? We cannot always improve services by trying to figure things out on our own. We also wonder how far both have to listen openly to each other? It can be hard work to listen, especially when we are feeling stressed, frustrated, busy, uncertain of ourselves and so on. Conversations about feelings, thinking and workplace action can be messy at times. Therefore we suggest that both parties have to be patient with each other. The mentor has to resist the temptation and impulse to tidy things up for their protégé. Both may have to reflect upon the benefits of being 'disturbed'. By this we mean having our cherished practices and ideas questioned. How can the mentoring process be a creative one if those involved are not willing to be disturbed?

In this book we want to present a different way of 'framing' the art of reflective mentoring. We want to suggest that there are four very important parts (or processes) encapsulated within the label 'reflective mentoring'. There are three origins of these processes. One is from our experiences of mentoring over 20 years. Another is from reviewing the large and compelling volume of evidence, accumulated in the international peer-reviewed journal *Reflective Practice*, in existence since 2000. The third source is an analysis of key mentoring research papers (for example Eby et al, 2006; Underhill, 2006). We suggest that, taken together, these form the positive core of reflective mentoring. This positive core helps focus attention, stimulate thinking, develop strengths-based conversations (not just deficit-based ones) and enable the protégé to take positive action. The processes are:

1. Developing an appreciative gaze: Consciously looking for and talking about what is good and successful in the protégés current working life

2. Re-framing experience: Talking about what needs to change — feelings, thoughts and practices — by exploring options and alternatives

3. Building practical wisdom: Listening to and learning from others and not only the mentor

4. Demonstrating achievement and moving forward: Documenting learning and using this as evidence to improve the protégé's practice and/or programmes and policy.

Figure 2.2 shows that ideally (but not always) the reflective mentoring process starts with *appreciation*. These appreciations begin a virtuous upward learning spiral (rather than a vicious downward spiral), which should provide the protégé with the confidence and courage to begin to learn more and different things. Re-framing helps enhance the protégés knowledge, skills and experience. The mentor needs to try to create a 'positive psychological space' so that their protégé focuses their energy on welcoming in, not on closing out. Welcoming in means that we have to let go of two bad habits that distort the re-framing process. Kahane (2004) calls these habits *reloading* and *downloading*. Reloading is when we are not truly and openly attending to what's happening, not really listening, empathizing or wanting to understand. What we are actually doing, when reloading, is rewinding some already existing mental tapes and rehearsing them in our mind. These are tapes that contain those things that we already know and ways we always behave. Downloading is when we re-produce (communicate) without alteration. There is no creativity associated with this. Downloading is no good for creating new insight and breakthroughs. When we download, we are deaf to others' experience and insensitive to other possibilities. We hear only that which confirms our own experiences. By welcoming in, we mean adopting a frame of mind that enables the protégé to develop their positive core of values and actions. Unlike downloading (saying what we always say, doing what we always do, thinking in the same old ways), welcoming in is about listening to, and learning from others who also have a stake in the healthcare system. It is learning from those who have different, even opposing, perspectives to our own. These may be from the mentor or from other protégés if the process is a more collegial (peer group) one. Welcoming in is wanting to develop new insight and experiencing the thrill of this. Fundamentally, it is learning that accrues from discovering what is new beyond our comfort zone. This re-framing purpose of reflective mentoring enables the protégé to actively develop their positive core of

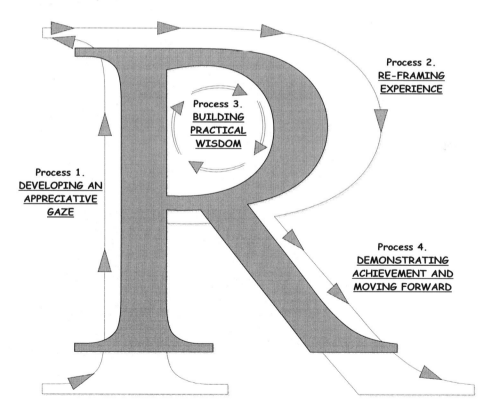

Figure 2.2 The positive core of reflective mentoring.

values and actions. This, in itself, may be regarded as an achievement.

In essence, the art of reflective mentoring is not forcing something to happen, but releasing something. Releasing the human spirit to appreciate what's good, best and right in clinical practice. Releasing the mind to see things in new and different ways. Releasing our sources of energy to build a positive core of values and (even better) actions. Releasing us from those things that serve to bind, silence and dis-empower us so that we can move forward with courage and greater wisdom.

So how might the positive core we are suggesting lead to a positive mentoring experience? Much depends upon the skilfulness of the mentor to ask **positive questions**. These can lead to positive conversations and hopefully to positive action. *Table 2.1* shows some of the kinds of positive questions that the mentor might wish to have, in their repertoire, when talking with their protégé. It shows questions that might be a catalyst for a constructive conversation. The first questions focus upon the individual (the protégé). The second shifts the focus to the protégé

Table 2.1   Some examples of positive questions at the heart of reflective mentoring

Main focus	Developing and appreciative gaze	Re-framing experience	Building practical wisdom	Demonstrate achievement and moving forward
The protégé	What do you feel you do really well and why?	What are some of your possibilities for improvement?	What are your core values? Why do you hold these?	How far are you able to put your values into action?
Their team	What are your team's talents and achievements? How can you play to your strengths?	How can you ask positive questions to develop more strengths-based conversations?	What are your team's values? Why do they hold these?	How can you create more opportunities to do what you do best, every day?
Their organisation	What are your organisation's major success stories? How can you amplify them?	What options and alternatives do you have to increase performance?	What are your organisation's values? What does your organisation stand for?	How far is performance aligned with mission?

within a work group or team. The third are positive questions that the protégé may wish to explore if they are coming to the mentor in a more organisational frame of mind. We are not suggesting that a reflective mentoring process requires a slavish working through some, or all of these questions. What we are suggesting is that a key characteristic of our view of reflective mentoring is the mentor's ability to draw upon and explore positive questions with their protégé.

Reflective mentoring as a purposeful activity

We suggest that reflective mentoring needs to be a purposeful activity. We are suggesting that it has four fundamental purposes. These are to be:

Appreciative: It needs to begin from a reflective conversation, between those involved, appreciating what works well, about achievement, success and the reasons for this. Reflective mentoring is therefore a strengths-based rather than a deficit-based approach. It needs to search for and celebrate the positive. For example what the protégé feels is working well and what they are proud of. Reflective mentoring doesn't require the protégé to (only) bring problems to the mentor. It is not just about problem-solving.

Generative: It is fuelled by forms of reflection-on-experience that gives both the mentor and the protégé the opportunity, and courage, to see freshly and with eyes wide open. This is often called a re-framing process, or looking at things in new or different ways. Re-framing is different from always seeing and understanding limited by routine and habit. In other words, seeing bounded by what we already know.

Transcending: It arises from asking questions that really matter – the 'frame-shifting questions'- that help those involved better understand who they are and why they think and act in the ways they do. These questions, which are a crucial feature of mentoring through conversation, and a skilful part of the reflective mentor's repertoire, when used judiciously, should help the protégé transcend fear, force and failure, oppressive, exclusive and exploitative work practices. These are the kinds of question that help build a positive core of values and actions. It is mentoring that is elevating, affirming and energising.

Transformative: Its potency accrues from the way the reflective conversation informs and transforms action and vice versa. This reciprocity provides the basis for useful learning. By this, we mean learning that can be put to good use in order to improve ourselves and the services we manage and deliver. It helps us achieve something more or different. It is mentoring that focuses on learning that helps us move forward.

Conclusion

In essence, the art of reflective mentoring is not forcing something to happen, but releasing something. Releasing the human spirit to appreciate what is good, best and right in clinical practice. Releasing the mind to see things in new and different ways. Releasing our sources of energy to build a positive core of values and (even better) actions. Releasing us from those things that serve to bind, silence and dis-empower us so that we can move forward with courage and greater wisdom. The power of the positive question plays a crucial role in helping to release this human spirit.

References

Anderson H, Cooperrider D, Gergen KJ, Gergen M, McNamee S, Whitney D (2006) *The Appreciative Organisation*. Taos Institute Publications, Chagrin Falls

Allen TD, Eby LT, Poteet ML, Lentz E, Lima L (2004) Career benefits associated with mentoring protégés: a meta-analysis. *Journal of Apllied Psycology* **89**: 127-136

Colley H (2002) A 'rough guide' to the history of mentoring from a Marxist feminist perspective. *Journal of Education for Teaching* **28**(3): 257-273

Collins J (2006) *Good to Great and the Social Sectors*. Random House Business Books, London

Delobbe N, Vandenberghe C (2001) La formation en enterprise comme dispositif de socialization organisationelle: Enquête dans le secteur bancaire. *Le Travail Humain* **64**: 61-89

Eby LT, Allen TD (2002) Further investigation of protégés' negative mentoring experiences. *Group and Organization Management* **27**: 456-479

Eby LT, McManus SE (2004) The protégé's role in negative mentoring experiences. *Journal of Vocational Behaviour*, 65, 255-275

Eby LT, Lockwood AL, Butts M (2006) Perceived support for mentoring: a multiple perspectives approach. *Journal of Vocational Behaviour* **68**: 267-291

Ensher EA, Murphy SE (2005) *Power Mentoring: How Successful Mentors and Protégés get the Most out of their Relationships*. Jossey-Bass, San Francisco

Feldman DC (1999) Toxic mentors or toxic protégés? A critical re-examination of dysfunctional mentoring. *Human Resource Management Review* **9**: 247-278

Finkenauer C, Engels RCME, Branje SJT, Meeus W (2004) Disclosure and relationship satisfaction in families. *Journal of Marriage and Family* **66**: 195-209

Ghaye T (2007) Is reflective practice ethical? (The case of the reflective portfolio). *Reflective Practice* **8**(2): 151-162

Ghaye T (2008) *Building the Reflective Healthcare Organisation*. Blackwell, Oxford

Ghaye T, Lillyman S (2007) *Effective Clinical Supervision: The Role of Reflection (2nd Edition)*. Quay Books Division, MA Healthcare Ltd, London

Johnson WB, Lall R, Holmes EK, Huwe JM, Nordlund MD (2001) Mentoring experiences among navy midshipmen. *Military Medicine* **166**(1): 27-31

Kahane A (2004) *Solving Tough Problems.* Berrett-Koehler Publishers, Inc., San Francisco

Lave J, Wenger E (1991) *Situated Learning: Legitimate Peripheral Participation.* Cambridge University Press, Cambridge

Martin RL (2003) *The Responsibility Virus.* Prentice Hall Financial Times, Harlow

Patrick KC (2002) Orphans and Olympians (Taking responsibility for starting a mentoring movement for young dancers). *Dance Magazine* **76**(2): 14

Ragins BR, Scandura TA (1999) Burden or blessing? Expected costs and benefits of being a mentor. *Journal of Organizational Behaviour* **20**: 493-509

Reis HT, Shaver P (1988) Intamacy as an interpersonal process. In: Duck SW, Hay DF, Hobfoll SE, Ickes W, Montgomery BM, eds. *Handbook of Personal Relationships: Theory, Research and Interventions.* John Wiley, Chichester, England: 267–389

Sprecher S, Hendrick SS (2004) Self-disclosure in intimate relationships: associations with individual and relationship characteristics over time. *Journal of Social and Clinical Psychology* **23**: 857-877

Strong M, Baron W (2004) An analysis of mentoring conversations with beginning teachers: suggestions and responses. *Teaching and Teacher Education* **20**: 47-57

Sundli L (2007) Mentoring — A new mantra for education? *Teaching and Teacher Education* **23**: 201-214

Underhill CM (2006) The effectiveness of mentoring programs in corporate settings: a meta-analytical review of the literature. *Journal of Vocational Behaviour* **68**: 292-307

Wallace JE (2001) The benefits of mentoring for female lawyers. *Journal of Vocational Behaviour* **58**(3): 366-391

Wanberg CR, Welsh ET, Kammeyer-Mueller J (2007) Protégé and mentor self-disclosure: levels and outcomes within formal mentoring dyads in a corporate context. *Journal of Vocational Behaviour* **70**: 398-412

Weaver MA, Chelladurai P (1999) A mentoring model for management in sport and physical education. *Quest* **51**(1): 24-38.

Wittenberg PM (1998) Successful mentoring in a correctional environment. *Federal Probation* **62**(2): 75-80

CHAPTER 3

Roles and responsibilities of the mentor and the protégé

In the first part of this book we reviewed the difference between the mentorship process and other supervisory roles within professional practice. Here we will concentrate on the role of the mentor and protégé and how reflection plays an important part of that process. To illustrate this we will draw on experiences from a variety of practice settings. We will review three aspects of the role of mentor: these include what a mentor needs to be, what the mentor knows, and what the mentor does.

The role of the protégé and how the mentor can influence their training and will be discussed in the second part of the chapter.

What a mentor might be

We have discussed the origins of the mentor role in the first chapter where they were seen mainly as the 'older and wiser' person. Here we will review some of the other characteristics of the mentor from the current research and professional literature. We note that even though the literature tells us what the mentor needs to be, there are fewer definitions as to what the mentor is.

Definitions of the mentor demonstrate how authors take on slightly different perspectives of the role. As we can see with Kramer back in 1974 who stated that a mentor was:

> '...a nurse who has the ability to integrate education and work values so that realistic strategies for resolving conflict maybe developed'.
>
> *Kramer (1974, p. 23)*

McIntyre and Hagger's definition reviews teaching, interpersonal and managerial skills when they sated that:

> '...[the] overall picture of mentor is of someone who both wears the good teachers mantle and has the interpersonal skills required as an effective manager of adults'.
>
> *McIntyre and Hagger (1996, p. 22)*

Klasen and Clutterbuck (2002) focus on the learning of the mentor so that the protégé becomes self-reliant on the acquisition of new knowledge, skills and abilities and develops a continuous motivation to learn.

Jarvis and Gibson (1997) also noted that mentors should be highly qualified people who enter into a one-to-one relationship of teaching and learning with junior colleagues in order to help them perform their role or develop and mature as human beings.

Lloyd Jones et al (2001) note other characteristics such as:

> *'...act as role model, facilitate the student's clinical learning experiences on the placement, undertake clinical teaching, supervise the student's work so as to ensure the quality of care and safety of all concerned, and assess the student's practice on that placement'.*
>
> *Lloyd Jones et al (2001, p. 152)*

When defining the role for medical students, Aagaard and Hauer (2003) suggested:

> *'...a more senior person within the medical training environment, with whom you have sustained, ongoing relationship. A mentor promotes your professional development by discussing your goals, needs and weaknesses and accomplishments A mentor should be more than a role model or advisor'.*
>
> *Aagaard and Hauer (2003, p. 298)*

Dodgson (1986) and Caldwell and Carter (1993) concluded that the definitions are elusive and varies according to the view of the author as we can see above. However Caldwell and Carter (1993) suggest that, no matter what the variations of the definition are, they fall into two categories: those that emphasize the professional development of the protégé, and those that emphasize professional and personal development of the protégé. Most mentors learn their role on the job and therefore feel inadequately prepared for it, according to Andrews and Chilton (2000). For this reason the Nursing and Midwifery Council note in their definition that an NMC mentor is a registrant who:

> *'...following successful completion of and NMC approved mentor preparation programme — facilitates learning, and supervises and assesses students in a practice settings'.*
>
> *NMC (2006, p. 17)*

This places the emphasis on a programme to develop this role.

Darling (1984), who was a pioneer in relation to mentoring in the US, concluded that a mentor had three absolute requirements for a successful mentoring role including:

- Attraction (mutual)
- Action (time and energy)
- Affect (mutual respect).

Darling (1984) also highlighted three basic roles of inspirer, investor and supporter from a list of 14 characteristics that included:

- Role model
- Envisioner
- Energiser
- Investor
- Supporter
- Challenger
- Standard-prodder
- Teacher
- Feedback-giver
- Eye-opener
- Door-opener
- Idea-bouncer
- Problem-solver
- Career counsellor.

Since these were published they have been developed as Gray and Smith (2000) noted some serious omissions in her published research and concluded that students viewed a mentor as someone who would support, guide, assess and supervise students. Other authors have added to Darling's (1984) list and included:

- Befriending (Suen and Chow, 2001)
- Self-assurance, clinically competent, sensitive to protégés needs, ideas, feeling and situation with the ability to criticise effectively with political savvy (Smith et al, 2001)
- Enthusiastic, approachable patient with a good sense of humour (Gray and Smith, 2000)
- To be a listener, mirror, advocate, provide structure and be able to celebrate (Northcott 2000).

The list foes on with each interpretation of the role, however Northcott (2000) sums the role up in two words as 'being there'.

We can include all these characteristics within the following headings, that a mentor needs to be:

- Responsible (taking care of their protégé)
- Committed (caring for their protégé)

- Competent professional practitioner (giving care to clients)
- Responsive (receiving care).

Responsible (taking care of the protégé)

The mentor needs to take responsibility for supporting and guidance of the protégé, whether they are in training or moving to a new area of work. The protégé will look towards their mentor for support in an environment that is often alien to them or for the qualified protégé for support on career moves within the wider professional arena. The different supporting roles were discussed in the first part of this book. Here, we will discuss some of the characteristics involving responsibility including befriending, being approachable, career counsellor and a good communicator.

Befriending

We also note that some mentorship experiences we have in training can affect the way we feel throughout our career. Whilst reading through some critical analysis accounts of mentoring experiences of qualified professionals on a mentorship course, many recounted situations related to the way they were introduced on the first day to the new workplace environment, mentor and staff. The impact of that greeting and how they were included in the workforce when at that time they felt very vulnerable is recorded years after the event. Where they had described a negative situation it was often where the mentor had not taken care of their protégé in the first few hours of the arrival in the workplace. The accounts included situations where the mentor had not shown them the layout of the ward, not including them in staff handovers, left them to find their own way around, including accounts of not offering them a cup of tea when other staff were having one. Often these incidents had gone on to affect their relationship with the mentor throughout that placement and had required a lot of work on both parts to build a meaningful relationship, although as we can see by these incidents the hurt remained for them years after the event.

The befriending role is important for the relationship to work for both parts, and is vital from the first meeting. Gray and Smith (2000) note that this must be done with genuine concern for the protégé. Suen and Chow (2001) put this role at the top of their list from their study of students' perceptions of the effectiveness of mentors and suggest that mentors do not fulfil the befriending role adequately.

We also note the role conflict between this and the role of assessment. If a mentor is expected to befriend then can they truly be objective in their assessment of the their protégé? However, we note that they are also best placed to take on the assessment role within practice placement areas.

Approachable

With the befriending role the mentor needs to be approachable and have good interpersonal skills. The protégé should feel safe in the relationship where they can give expression to their thoughts and feelings, destabilize and not be made to feel incompetent (Trubowitz and Robins, 2003).

Career counsellor

Sometimes students may use a mentor after they have qualified to help them adjust to their new role and later in life when they return for advice and guidance in where they should go and develop throughout their professional career. Trubowitz and Robins (2003) noted that mentors not only guide and orientate new teachers but also keep them in the profession.

Mentors can also help the protégé to balance their social and professional life (Aagaard and Haver, 20003) and need to possess some counselling skills such as listening and being a resource for additional specialist help should an individual require it.

Communicator

Being a communicator is one of the main roles required by the mentor. If they are to be teachers and guide, then they need the skills to communicate with those they are supporting. Being a mentor includes teaching the protégé and assisting them to relate the theory into the work place.

Committed (caring about their protégé)

We have discussed some of the roles of the mentor in 'caring for' in the above section, but this role involves 'caring about'; treating a protégé with respect for them as a person and being sensitive to them as a practitioner and learner. As Earnshaw (1995) noted, many students still see the mentor as a matriarchal/patriarchal figure whose purpose is to smooth their passage through a period of time. As noted above we can care for the protégé and fulfil this matriarchal/patriarchal role, or we can care about the protégé and prepare them for their professional carer and give them the skills for life long learning. The characteristics included in this aspect include those of being an investor, sensitive, motivator, challenger, critical thinker, reflector, problem-solver, eye-opener, assessor, feedback-giver, idea-bouncer and door-opener.

We also note the danger of the mentors who are what Darling (1984) calls 'dumpers'. These are those mentors who have the philosophy of throwing students in a the deep end and abdicate all responsibility for the student and their learning.

Investor

Without investment in the role and the person they are supporting the mentor cannot gain or give their best. One of the main concerns is that of time and emotional commitment and the mentor should be aware of this before taking on the role (Smith et al, 2001). For the role to be effective many mentors feel the pressure of taking on students as an extra burden to an already demanding job. Managers who have added responsibilities within the workplace may not have the time to commit to the protégé and also may be removed from their needs as a learner. A mentor therefore needs to be someone who has consolidated their own learning and is competent in their role but not too far removed from the needs of the protégé.

Sensitive

The mentor not only has to understand the requirements for their protégé, but also needs to be sensitive to those needs (Smith et al, 2001). They need to understand other pressures protégés have to deal with such as academic, family or political pressures that might affect their learning.

Motivator

A mentor should be keen and enthusiastic about their professional practice but at the same time remain realistic to their expectations of their protégé (Gray and Smith, 2000). In order to motivate others the mentor should believe in, and have a genuine interest, about their own work. The mentor needs to believe in the learner and their own teaching role so that others can continue the practice. A good motivator will encourage their protégé to move boundaries and set standards of professional practice.

Challenger/teacher

In the past an apprenticeship approach to mentorship in the workplace involved 'learning from Nellie', where rituals were passed onto the learner through observation. However, work-based learning cannot be assumed (Billet, 2000).

With the development of teaching approaches and an adult/partnership approach to learning, the mentor and protégé work together to produce a 'knowledgeable doer' who integrates theory. As stated, the mentor role is more than a guide to see people through a period of time. The role involves mutual respect with the ability to provoke, challenge and present the protégé with unfamiliar situations, providing a problem based reflective approach and setting goals for the protégé (Earnshaw, 1995).

The mentor may include more formal teaching opportunities in their approach, however they also need to facilitate reflective practice and become a door-opener

(Jarvis and Gibson, 1997) In order to fulfil this role the mentor needs to be familiar with the course programme or role requirements to assist their protégé.

Critical thinker

> *'Doing without thinking may be dangerous and doing and thinking without feeling is practically impossible'.*
>
> *Scheffer and Rubenfield (1999, p. 56)*

These skills of critically thinking involves feeling and needs to be developed within the protégé as the mentor seeks to differentiate between assumptions and fact, are open to new alternative ways of looking at and behaving in the professional world (Welsh and Swann, 2002). Together, the mentor and protégé can exert effort towards gathering new information and become excited at the prospect of discovery and developing life-long learner skills (Schaffer and Rubenfield, 1999).

Reflector

A profession will not develop without practitioners being able to reflect on practice and move that forward in a constructive approach. Although we note that reflection is not a panacea to solving the problems of linking theory to practice in the workplace, the consensus is that reflection offers many benefits for the protégé (Johns and Freshwater, 1997).

In this case the mentor's role is to develop those reflective skills within their protégé. This approach will involve problem based learning, clinical supervision, the use of learning journal, critical incident and critical conversations (Ghaye and Lillyman, 2006).

Central also is the ability to critically think about practice. The protégé should develop their own justifications and practical principles from their work demanding a shift in the role of the mentor to becoming co-enquirers with a more equal and open relationship (Kerry and Mayes, 1995).

Problem-solver

As noted above, the mentor needs to have a problem-solver approach to practice. This is related to the reflective process and the ability to review practice and develop and change practice.

Eye-opener

Often a student or trainee may feel that they are already well-established in their training and just want to get on and pass a particular placement. The mentor can open their eyes to all sorts of new experiences, ways of reviewing the workplace and taking more strategic or political view of the work.

Assessor

Wiles (2006) notes the importance of assessment remaining objective and analytical rather than subjective. As noted above, the roles of assessor can cause some conflict with that of befriending.

The mentor may also seek help and support from their academic colleagues and there is a need for partnership between the practice place and higher educational establishment.

Feedback-giver

Students often complain that there is little reward given when things are going well, but only commented on when things go wrong. As with the theories of teaching, people need to be praised and have some reassurance of their performance in order to develop. Without the support and reflection they can be learning the wrong practice or not developing to their full potential. The mentor should treat the protégé as an adult and use constructive critical feedback to enforce praise, reflection to support the protégé.

Idea-bouncer

As part of the reflective process the mentor can act as an idea-bouncer with their protégé. It is not always good to have the answers for the protégé but to allow them to develop reflective skills in their approach to practice.

Door-opener

The mentor might not feel that they have all the answers for the protégé, however they can show them the right doors to push and even open some for them. With guidance the mentor can be active in their protégés career and support them through it.

Standard-setter

The mentor also needs to be specialists in their own field and be a standard-setter. However, Ryle (1963) noted the danger of being more concerned with competence than with cognitive repertoires. The mentor needs to balance the course requirements with observing the student, providing feedback and pushing their boundaries. This process necessitates the student also taking responsibility. The protégé can however fall into the trap of once achieving the competency they can stop learning.

We can see some of the characteristics in the following incident of the labelled 'lazy student'.

The lazy student!

Whilst working on the ward it was noted that the student was sitting down at the desk looking bored and not enjoying their placement. On questioning the student stated that she felt they were learning little as staff were too busy and left the student to do their own thing. There was plenty going on and the student had been involved with washing and dressing the patients, but now was sitting around as everyone was too busy to assist with her. Later the mentor stated that the perception of the student was that she was lazy and not willing to work.

On reflecting on this situation, it is obvious that the ward was busy, and although the mentor was in charge she did not have time to teach and guide the student. Mentorship takes on many forms, and one thing that some mentors fail to note is the value of role modelling. The student picks up far more whilst observing the mentor and watching their reactions to the way they interact with the patients and staff. This involves less time than the formal teaching that the mentor wanted to give. Both the student and mentor needed to communicate and identify how they could work more together responding to the needs of the ward but at the same time meeting the needs of the student and mentor. Having time out to review and reflect the situation the student could have been invited to observe the mentor therefore reducing the feeling of boredom and the student would not be labelled as 'lazy' when in reality she had wanted to get involved.

Competent professional practitioner (giving care)

For this aspect there are other characteristics that need to be developed by the mentor, and these include: role model, being self-aware, an envisioner, energiser, and standard setter with a good sense of humour.

Role model

One of the major roles noted by many of the authors is that of the role modelling and is often at the top of the list of characteristics for the mentor (Darling, 1984; Lloyd Jones et al, 2001). The role model then is someone who leads by example but is not a dual role where part of the time is given to teaching and part to practice, but both parts are carried out simultaneously (Wong and Wong, 1987; Canham, 1998). However some students have reported where they have learnt through a negative experience by seeing a mentor do things they would not want to repeat. If the mentor relies totally on role modelling as an approach to mentorship they are in danger of disempowering the student, and as Armitage and Burnard (1991) note, of the protégé becoming dependant and conforming to practice.

A good role model does not attempt to project their experiences onto the protégé but encourages them to develop their own experiences, reflect and learn from them. Mentors need to practice what they state and demonstrate that through their own practice. However, Aagaard and Hauer (2003) noted that a mentor needs to be more than just a role model and so mentors need to develop the other characteristics. As Sullivan (2000) notes, the larger role of mentor as to:

> '...enable the mentee (protégé) to reflect on actions and perhaps to modify future actions as a result, it is about enabling behavioural and attitudinal change'.
>
> Sullivan (2000, p. 163)

Self-aware

Mentors need insight to their own behaviour, attitude, and values they display in their practice. They need to think about how they teach and their attitudes, reflection on their own practice with analysis of the teaching process (Lopez Real and Kwan, 2005).

Envisioner/engerizer

As stated earlier, the mentor needs to be motivated in their own role and in doing so can engage their protégé in their approach. Goal-setting with the protégé can help provide direction and development for the protégé, thereby providing new approaches to learning. The mentor needs to take pride in expanding a protégés work prowess and in so gives back to the profession (Darwin, 2000).

Responsive (receiving care)

Often the mentor is giving of themselves caring for the protégé and client without receiving care for themselves and support from others. This can be fulfilled through supportive processes such as clinical supervision or practice support (Ghaye and Lillyman, 2007). Support can also come form their mentor. In the situation below we see a situation where the mentor cares for and about their protégé, whilst at the same time giving care to their client. However the mentor found that she herself required some support and time for reflection to receive some care.

The experienced student

A student was out with her mentor — who was a district nurse — visiting patients in the home. The student had a military background and was constantly informing the district nurse of all that they had achieved and seen on the battlefield. The district nurse was uneasy as she had not had experience in such traumatic situations, and began to doubt her own ability in their role as mentor and nurse. As the day wore on the partnership was deteriorating to the point where the district nurse lacked confidence in her own ability to carry out the role of mentor and district nurse. The district nurse then sought help from her own mentor who was able to help her review her own skills and abilities as a mentor and nurse. On discussion and reflection they were able to identify that it was potentially the student's fear of nursing within the community and that was making him express assertion and maintaining an air of authority.

During the following occasion that the district nurse and student were out together they were able to discuss issues relating to community nursing. Opportunity was given to the student to express their fears, and the relationship developed, resulting in a positive learning experience of mentoring and community nursing. The situation may have led the district nurse to have total confidence failure in her own practice, and if not careful it could actually affect the care she gives clients.

One aspect that so often is lacking is where the mentor can then gain his or her own mentorship. Pope et al (2003) revealed the need for more structured support for the mentor to fulfil their role as supervisors and assessors in a range of practice settings. Some professionals are asked to give with no support for themselves. Each person needs to be developed and this might take the form of another mentor that they can approach. As you move on you might find that you have different mentors for different parts of your lives. One person might support you with career moves, another with academic study and another in the practical aspect of you work. You might be fortunate enough to find that quality in one person.

Some things a mentor needs to know

The literature argues that mentors require some form of training for the role (NMC, 2006), and it is not expected that experience as a protégé or in practice can result in the mentor taking on that role efficiently.

In Gould et al's (2001) study, when asking managers about their preparation as mentors, 65% ($n = 99$) reported poor preparation was given before undertaking this role. This is supported by Andrews and Chilton (2000), who suggest that preparation varies from observing others to more formal training.

The mentor also needs to know where they can get support from within the work environment and from external organisations where the student maybe taking their studies. Training and mentorship is a partnership between the institution and the work base.

In one study, Davis et al (1995) noted that three quarters of mentors were not undertaking continuing professional development, most were unable to articulate what they did, and critical thinking skills were not developed in these professionals.

Some things a mentor does

What a mentor does can have a great impact on the rest of their protégé's career. Recently reviewing many reflections on the mentorship process from students undertaking a mentorship course the students mainly referred back to experiences in their own training days where they had experienced both positive and negative aspects of mentorship. Now years after these experiences they are recalled by the now trainee mentors and the impact those experiences had on their own role.

Sometimes in the business of the work environment we can forget how vulnerable the new student/trainee feels. That first few minutes to settle down, introduce the team and show them where to go makes the world of difference. The impact of these minutes makes the difference to the placement and the career.

Skilled mentor awakens and encourages and nurtures the student without making them feel threatened or patronised (Scheffer and Rubenfield, 1999).

Northcott (2000) advocates providing structure celebrating setting tasks. We can see this in the following incident of the student practitioner.

The student practitioner

Many students in the healthcare setting take up part-time jobs within practice to support their income. This can lead to some role conflict where one day the student is an unqualified practitioner and counted in the numbers, and the next day a student with a supernumerary status. This may result in confusion not only for the student but also for the mentor — who has to adapt roles.

A student was on a placement on a ward where she also worked as a rehabilitation assistant. The student reported a positive staff attitude towards her as a student. Initially she had expected to carry on with the role of rehabilitation assistant — a role she had done for many years — and be passed over as a student, thus missing many learning opportunities. However, this was not the case and the student felt that the mentor had bought both roles together thereby providing the student with a valuable learning experience.

Benefits for the mentor

Although there is little in the literature to support the benefits to the mentor, in their study Lopez Real and Kwan (2005) noted that 70% of their mentors claimed that they had benefited professionally from mentoring. These aspects of professional development they noted included learning through: self-reflection, from students, through mutual collaboration, and from the university staff. There can be a mutual learning, and Clutterbuck (2001) and Watson (2004) noted in their study that it 58% noted it enhanced job prospects.

Benefits for the organisation

If students/trainees and newly qualified staff feel valued and supported in their respective roles then recruitment and retention, increased motivation, management of corporate culture, leadership and development will be improved (Clutterbuck, 2001).

The role of the protégé

The protégé, according to Northcott (2000), is someone in training, returning to practice, adaptation programme, newly qualified, newly upgraded or established practitioners. Klasen and Clutterbuck (2002) agree with this, stating that it is one of the best methods to enhance individuals learning and development throughout all walks of life.

Much of the literature talks about the mentor and their role, however the protégé needs to take some responsibility for their learning and development.

The role of the protégé can affect practitioners' view of their career and practice. Whilst reading many accounts of the mentoring process from students on mentoring programmes, there is a common element identified in the incidents recorded of how mentoring was used within their own training.

Trainees and students view the role of mentorship in different ways, and it is up to the mentor to respond as they see fit. Sometimes the student needs someone to identify with and be guided by as in their first placement visit, and other times feel more confident and just need an identified person to ask for help when required.

Why do I need a mentor?

Many times we can embark on different situations in life where we feel we are well equipped to face what life will throw at us. The case below shows how supporting and helping someone through a particular time could have turned out so much differently if they had not had the support from a mentor when working as a volunteer.

The volunteer

A nurse had gone to work in a foreign country for a three-year period. Having visited the country on several previous visits she felt that she could cope and work in the culture and environment with little support. On arrival she was sent to a camp to work with deprived children away from the city, which she knew would happen. However, living in a foreign land without any other person who spoke the same language or came from the same culture was very different. After living and working at a children's home for about six months, the nurse was emotionally and physically exhausted, and the need for a mentor and support was identified. There was no support and no one to turn to within the organisation and the only person that showed some concern and understanding was from outside.

Although this particular person could not be a role model, there were many other roles that they were able to fulfil. Primarily, this 'mentor' was a native of the country and was able to communicate very well in the mother tongue of the nurse (the 'protégé'). Being removed from the everyday frustrations and politics of the work, during the weekly meetings the mentor invested time and energy to reflect on decisions that had been made during the previous week and identify areas for development. Although the mentor was not an expert in the work of the nurse, the mentor became a critical friend and could understand, could teach and explain the local culture. The experience turned into a good learning experience that, without the mentor, may well have resulted in a very different outlook of the protégé to the work and their emotional outcome.

From the story above we can unpick some of the characteristics identified in the beginning of the chapter displayed by the mentor in the supporting the protégé. The first main characteristic was the ability to communicate with each other. This is an extreme case where there were two different languages being used. However, most of us can identify with that in our own professions where there is a lot of jargon used. The trainee who does not understand the different terms may as well be like the volunteer in a foreign land. Communication is one of the main and critical aspects of any mentor/protégé relationship, that they understand each other and that the mentor can translate the language for other people.

In the case above the mentor also took on the role of critical friend, and although did not always agree with the work that was being done still offered support and time for reflection. The teaching aspect came in the form of the cultural aspects of the country and the ability to critically reflect on the impact that it was having on the way the protégé worked and behaved. The mentor was able to challenge the protégé and make her think about the practice and decisions that were made as a part of the work. Counselling skills were a very important aspect of this relationship.

Some things a protégé needs to be

A protégé needs to be committed to the role of learner at whatever stage of their career, they need to be loyal to their mentor and organisation, and possess sincerity, honesty warmth and empathy (Shay and Stallings, 1993). Smith et al (2001) provide a list of the characteristic of the protégé, stating that they to be ambitious to get on in their career, appreciate people, resources and what has been given to them, be willing to ask for help, and demonstrate an interest in the subject thereby forming a bond with their mentor. Other characteristics they note are to be critically self-aware, to be able to disclose frustrations, listen, trust and accept advice, and be willing to learn from the mentor.

Some things a protégé needs to know

The protégé should understand the programme they are undertaking or have insight into the job they wish to develop in. At the beginning of the relationship, the protégé should bring with them some objectives of their own that will help the mentor provide the best learning situation for that individual.

Conclusion

A mentor's task is to assist the protégé to unleash their capacity to appreciate their strengths and meet challenges/problems constructively. Additionally, they should help the student arrive to high quality decisions by being supportive, challenging and, above all, helping their protégés to reflect. The protégé, in return, has a duty to the mentor, organisation and self to learn and develop their practice and expertise.

References

Aagaard EM, Hauer KE (2003) A Cross Sectional Descriptive study of mentoring relationships formed by medical students. *Journal of General Internal Medicine* **18**: 298-302

Andrews M, Chilton F (2000) Student and Mentor preparation of mentoring effectiveness. *Nurse Education Today* **20**: 555-562

Armitage P, Burnard P (1991) Mentors or Preceptors? Narrowing the Theory Practice Gap. *Nurse Education Today* **11**: 225-229

Billet S (2000) Guided Learning at work. *Journal of Workplace Learning* **12**(7): 272-285

Caldwell BJ, Carter EMA (1993) *The Return of the Mentor. Strategies for the Workplace Learning.* The Falmer Press London

Canham J (1998) Educational clinical Supervision: Meeting the needs of Speicalsit Community Practice Students and Professional Practice. *Nurse Education Today* **18**: 394-398

Clutterbuck D (2001) *Everyone Needs a Mentor: Fostering Talent at Work (3rd edition).* Chartered Institute of Personnel and Development, London

Darling LAW (1984) What do Nurses Want in a Mentor? *The Journal of Nursing Administration*

October: 42-44

Darwin A (2000) Critical Reflections on Mentoring in work Settings. *Adult Education Quarterly* **50**: 197-211

Davies S, Shepherd B, Thompson A, Whittaker K (1995) *An Investigation into the Changing Educational needs of Community Nurse, Midwives and Health Visitors in relation to the Teaching and Supervising and Assessing of Pre and Post Registration Students.* English National Board, London

Dodgson J (1986) Do Women in Education Need Mentors? *Education Canada* **Spring**: 29

Earnshaw GJ (1995) Mentorship: The Students' View. *Nurse Education Today* **15**: 274-279

Ghaye T, Lillyman S (2006) *Learning Journals and Critical Incidents (2nd Edition).* Quay Books, London

Ghaye T, Lillyman S (2007) *Effective Clinical Supervision (2nd Edition).* Quay Books, London

Gould D, Kelly D, Goldstone L (2001) Preparing Nurse Managers to Mentor Students. *Nursing Standard* **16**(11): 39-42

Gray MA, Smith LN (2000) The Qualities of an Effective Mentor from the Student Nurse's Perspective: Findings form a longitudinal Qualitative Study. *Journal of Advanced Nursing* **32**(6): 1542-1549

Jarvis P, Gibson S (1997) *The Teacher Practitioner in Nursing Midwifery and Health Visiting (2nd Ed).* Thornes, Cheltenham

Johns C, Freshwater D (1997) *Transforming Nursing through Reflective Practice.* Blackwell Science, Oxford

Kerry T, Mayes AS (1995) *Issues in Mentoring.* The Open University Press, Milton Keynes

Klasen N, Clutterbuck D (2002) *Implementing Mentoring Schemes: A Practical Guide to Successful Programmes.* Butterworth-Heinemann, Oxford

Kramer M (1974) *The Reality Shock. Why Nurses Leave Nursing.* Mosby, St Louise, Missouri

Lloyd Jones M, Walters S, Akehurst R (2001) The Implications of contact with the mentor for pre registration nursing and midwifery students. *Journal of Advanced Nursing* **35**(2): 151-160

Lopez Real F, Kwan T (2005) Mentors' Per captions of their own Professional Development during Mentoring. *Journal of Education for Teaching* **31**(1): 15-24

MacIntyre D, Hagger H (1996) *Mentors in Schools, Developing the Profession of teaching.* David Fulton Pubs, London

Northcott N (2000) Mentorship in Nursing. *Nursing Management* **7**(3): 30-32

Nursing and Midwifery Council (2006) *Standards to Support Learning and Assessment in Practice.* NMC, London

Pope R, Graham L, Finnerty G, Magnusson, C (2003) *An Investigation of the preparation and assessment for midwifery practice within a range of settings. Project report.* University of Surrey

Ryle G (1963) *The Concept of Mind.* Peregrine, London

Scheffer BK, Rubenfield MG (1999) *Clinical Thinking in Nursing and Interactive Approach (2nd edition).* Lippencott, Philadelphia

Shay S, Stallings K (1993) Institute for Nursing Excellence: A Retention Model. *Journal of Continuing Education in Nursing* **24**(2): 66-68

Smith LS, McAllister LE, Snype-Crawford C (2001) Mentoring Benefits and Issues for Public Health Nurses. *Public Health Nursing* **18**(2): 101-107

Suen LKP, Chow FLW (2001) Students' Perceptions of Effectiveness of Mentors in an Undergraduate Nursing Programme in Hong Kong. *Journal of Advanced Nursing* **36**(4): 505-511

Sullivan R (2000) Entrepreneurial Learning and Mentoring. *International Journal of Entrepreneurial Behaviour and Research* **6**(3): 160-175

Trubowitz S, Robins M (2003) *The Good Teacher Mentor: Setting the Standard for Support and Success.* Teachers College Press, New York

Watson S (2004) Mentorship Preparation: Reasons for undertaking the course and expectations of candidates. *Nurse Education Today* **24**(1): 30-40

Welsh I, Swann C (2002) *Partners in Learning: A Guide to Support and Assessment in Nurse Education.* Radcliff Medical Press. Oxford

Wiles Z (2006) The Student Mentor relationship. A Review of the Literature. *Nursing Standard* **20**(37): 42-47

Wong J, Wong S (1987) Towards Effective Clinical Teaching in Nursing. *Journal of Advanced Nursing* **12**: 505-513

CHAPTER 4

Reflective mentoring as using your appreciative intelligence

How does a mentor skillfully engage with a protégé if their morale and their trust in the system were low? If we spun the question around I wonder what it would do with our answer? For example, instead of focusing on present problems and things we want to get rid of (for example low morale and low trust), we should ask the question: '*How can the future emerge from the positive aspects of the present situation?*'. This gets us to focus on the good things that we are feeling and doing at this present time. This often takes a bit of mental discipline. For example, we often have conversations with our protégés about high staff turnover within their team, about experienced people leaving and newcomers arriving. These conversations can often begin quite negatively. The instinctive starting point for some protégés is that this is bad because it means 'more work for me'. Or that 'the skill-mix is upset and jobs do not get done as effectively'. A reframed reaction might be: '*This could be good because the new people are bringing into the team fresh energy, new ideas, and optimism. Maybe the optimism will be contagious*'.

In a nutshell, appreciative intelligence (or PN, as we shall now call it so that it does not get confused with AI which is appreciative inquiry) is about our ability to reframe a given situation and, in doing so, recognise the positive possibilities embedded in it.

PN also involves action: the necessary action to engage with others so that valued outcomes unfold from positive aspects of the current situation. PN is situated in the field of multiple intelligences, something proposed by Gardner (1993). Gardner (1993) demonstrated that intelligence was not a single ability but a number of capacities. He based his view on findings from disciplines such as anthropology, psychology and from the biographies of exceptional individuals. Thatchenkery and Metzker (2006) argue that PN is another type of intelligence within the multiple intelligence field. They argue that there are three parts to appreciative intelligence. These are our ability to:

- Reframe the current situation
- Appreciate the positive in the current situation
- Understand how the future unfolds from the positive present.

Certain personal qualities are needed for all this to happen. For example, we need to be persistent, have self-belief, have a tolerance for uncertainty, and have irrepressible resilience:

> *'Because the people we interviewed could re-frame, appreciate the positive and see how the future could unfold from the present, they could see how their end goal was possible to accomplish. Thus, they were willing to persist and to believe that their own actions and abilities would take them to a successful conclusion. Because they could envision the way a positive future could unfold from the present, they could deal with the uncertainty that often accompanies a new venture...or a crisis. They exhibited irrepressible resilience, the ability to bounce back from a difficult situation, as the result of re-framing, seeing what was positive in the situation, and understanding that a better future could come about despite a crisis or setback'.*
>
> *Thatchenkery and Metzker (2006, p. 15–16)*

Self-belief and a mentor's expectations

We suggest that the reflective mentor needs more than a belief that the future can unfold from the positive present. The mentor also needs to understand other kinds of belief embraced by the phrase 'self-fulfilling prophecy'.

Galatea Effect

Kierein and Gold (2000) describe three kinds of self-fulfilling prophecy. The first is called the *Galatea Effect*. This is about self-belief. It means that if we believe we can succeed, it is more likely that we will. If we believe we can think positively, no matter how troublesome the current situation is, then it is more likely that we will. The *Galatea Effect* is all about the expectations we have of ourselves. Some people seem to have this quality of strong self-belief. They trust themselves to succeed. They take an optimistic view of most situations and see 'failures' as learning opportunities. They turn problems into positive challenges. They are able to make problems their friends. It follows therefore that a mentor needs to enable their protégé to access this positive state of mind. For some protégés, of course, this may take some time and patience particularly if they are carrying a lot of 'negative baggage'. Or if they feel burdened down with the things that go on around them, which may make it difficult for them to do their best work. This *Galatea Effect* is all about what we think of ourselves.

Pygmalion Effect

A second effect is called the *Pygmalion Effect*. This is about the belief others have in us. For example, if a mentor conveys a clear message to their protégé that they think they will succeed at something, then they create a possibility that the protégé just might be successful!

The *Pygmalion Effect* is different, but linked in an interesting way to the *Galatea Effect*. For example in Greek mythology Pygmalion was a Cypriot king who was deeply in love with Aphrodite, the goddess of beauty and love. Pygmalion was rejected by the goddess so he sculptured an ivory image of her and went to bed with it. When Aphrodite saw this she was so touched that she let the sculpture come alive, and so the beautiful woman Galatea was born, and the couple had many children.

More recently, this effect is beautifully described in George Bernard Shaw's play *Pygmalion*. In the play, Professor Henry Higgins insists that a cockney flower girl called Eliza Doolittle can be transformed into a lady with some intense training in speech and deportment and by wearing the right clothes. He succeeds in this. However, the main point of the play is eloquently stated when Eliza talks to Professor Higgins' friend Colonel Pickering. Eliza says: *'You see, really and truly, apart from the things anyone can pick up (the dressing and the proper way of speaking and so on), the difference between a lady and a flower girl is not how she behaves, but how she is treated. I shall always be a flower girl to Professor Higgins, because he always treats me as a flower girl, and always will, but I know I can be a lady to you because you always treat me as a lady, and always will'.*

The expectations that mentors have of their protégés, and the protégés expectations of themselves, are two key factors in how well they perform at work. Both the Galatea and the Pygmalion Effects enable protégés to 'achieve and move forward' in response to the mentor's message that they are capable of success and a self-belief that they expect to succeed themselves (see *Figure 2.2*). Both are based on the feeling that nothing is impossible. The Galatea Effect can be expressed as: 'I know I can do this'. The Pygmalion Effect can be expressed as: 'I know you can do it'. The idea is not that the mentor manipulates their protégé by conveying deceptive messages, rather it is a way of bringing out the best in others by treating them respectfully, supportively and optimistically, by valuing and appreciating their gifts and talents, by remembering that change can be a bumpy process, and by reminding the person that things can get worse before they improve and that there is some value in stability.

Golem Effect

However, what happens if a protégé does not believe they can succeed at something they know they should be better at doing? Alternatively, what happens if their mentor has a loss of confidence, or lack of belief in them? In this case the positive self-fulfilling process we describe may turn into something else. The mentoring process may turn into a third kind of self-fulfilling prophecy. It is the negative one of the three we are describing here and it is called the *Golem Effect*. Mentors and protégés need to be aware of this.

Let's consider how it might work. A mentor might have low expectations of their protégé. This may be due to a variety of reasons. For example, they may not have got off to a good start in their mentoring process. This impression may get reinforced if the protégé comes across as somewhat pessimistic, negative, blaming or half-hearted in some way, that they do not exude any kind of enthusiasm, for some reason, about the mentoring process, or for their work. The mentor then begins to wonder if their protégé really has their heart in their work and in the process, whether the protégé is in the best place in the organization, doing the best they can. The mentor's verbal and non-verbal communication conveys a lack of confidence in the attitude and abilities of the protégé. This doubt leads the mentor to become over-responsible. The protégé, of course, notices their mentors' reservations and begins to sense a loss of trust. They may start doubting their own judgment and competence, so the mentor and protégé begin to get themselves tangled up in an unhelpful relationship that is fuelled by negative expectations. In short, the *Golem Effect* is simply this. If we expect people to do badly, it is likely they will not disappoint us! If the mentor conveys low expectations, the protégé can end up believing that their own comfort zone is the right and only place for them. If the mentor conveys unrealistic expectations, the protégé may end up believing that they are a low or under-achiever, and that they always fall short of other's expectations! Mentors need to believe their protégés can do something before they decide that they cannot do it. And yes, there is a chance that things might not succeed and work out as those involved had hoped. Both parties might be disappointed, but what is the alternative?

The Golem Effect is made worse if, for example, a mentor does not recognize the effort a protégé has made to improve an aspect of their practice, or if they fail to 'see' and to 'celebrate' their protégé's achievements (see *Figure 2.2*). This is why understanding and applying the positive core of reflective mentorship, as we describe it in this book, is so fundamental to successful mentoring. It is about a mentor and protégé reflecting-on-practice in order to appreciate the positive aspects of the protégés present situation. It is about mentors communicating positive thoughts and saying positive things to their protégés. About mentors seeing every protégé as having the ability to make a positive contribution at work and telegraphing that message.

We do not mean to over-simplify these effects. Many other factors also contribute to the quality of a protégés performance at work, how they feel about their job and how they see their future. Some significant influences are tied up in the collective term, organizational culture (Ghaye, 2008). What we are saying though is that a key characteristic of our view of reflective mentoring is that it is a process that emphasises improving what the protégé does well, rather than a process that focuses only on their faults and failings. Interestingly, Handy (1999) talked to a range of extraordinary characters, from Trevor Baylis and Richard Branson to Jane Tewson and Terence Conran. When reflecting on his conversations with them he thought: '*What drives people to create something from nothing? Is it ambition, the need for self-fulfilment? Is it to do with money, power, or even genes?'*. A significant finding was that successful business and social entrepreneurs talked of having someone, in their background, who believed in them no matter what. This is a vital role for every reflective mentor.

How mentors can use their appreciative intelligence

Orem et al (2007) talk about the power of asking appreciative questions. This is a key skill for a reflective mentor. These are not just any questions, but questions that are carefully phrased that grab our attention because our motivation to explore them supersedes whatever is going on, at work, right now.

We wonder if you can think of a recent question that did this for you? Here is an example of one that engages our own protégés every time:

'What is giving you most joy and satisfaction in your work right now?'.

In our mentoring roles we have found that this question makes each protégé curious about themselves, their colleagues and the places where they work. It helps them focus on what they most enjoy in their work, get wrapped up in, lose themselves in and look forward to, and the kind of things they would like to talk to us about for hours.

In contrast, let us imagine that a mentor asks their protégé to list their three most important work goals for the next six months. Although we know this could be an important thing to do, even appropriate in certain circumstances, arguably it just does not engage us in the same way. The approach to reflective mentoring which we are espousing in this book, which is in essence an appreciative one, assumes that the questions a mentor might ask their protégé encourages them to think about the present positively, and to build the future from the positive present. This re-connects us with the positive core of reflective mentoring that we set out in *Chapter 2* of this book. There we argued that reflective mentoring needed to be a purposeful activity. We then went on to describe its four fundamental processes. They are to develop appreciations, re-frame experience, build a positive core of values and actions (that constitutes practical wisdom), and then to put all this to good use by striving to achieve something more or different. In doing so, a sense of movement, hopefully forward, might be felt.

1. Develop appreciations

Our view takes us beyond the work of Schön (1983) and Dewey (1933) and the focus on 'problems' as an initial stimulus for reflection. We are drawing on the more recent work on appreciative inquiry (Cooperrider and Whitney, 2005) and appreciative intelligence (Thatchenkery and Metzker, 2006). This first process of reflective mentoring is about asking the kinds of question that deepens the protégés appreciation of their work with and for others. Appreciation of their own and others' gifts, talents, limitations, self-worth, identity, role, responsibilities and accountability. It is about asking questions to enable the protégé to develop a deeper understanding of their own learning agenda, self-knowledge and self-efficacy.

2. Re-frame experience

Here the process is not only to use the practices of reflection to generate, share, manage and utilise knowledge that arises through the mentoring conversation, but something more. The critical attribute of this second process of reflective mentoring is to re-frame (where appropriate) what the protégé discloses to the mentor (or other protégés if the process is a more collegial one). Re-framing means trying to look at things in a new or different way, to make the familiar a bit strange and to be open to the way this may open up alternatives for future thinking and action. For the process of reflective mentoring, re-framing is about trying to build-on from a valid picture of what is good and positive within the present, no matter how small, or apparently insignificant, this might be perceived. Re-framing can be supported by drawing upon diary or journal entries that a protégé might keep, or material in a protégé's reflective portfolio. The mentor's skilfulness is in enabling the protégé to anchor learning about what currently works and the root causes of this success. Reflective mentoring then is about amplifying the positive and enabling the protégé to grow in the direction of their strengths. It is not just about problem-posing, problem-solving, 'fixing' and trying to 'get rid' of things.

We are going to spend a bit more time explaining the process of re-framing as it is so central to mentors using their appreciative intelligence. In *Table 4.1* we set out 10 statements. In the middle column we list one interpretation of the first three. An un-appreciative interpretation or even one that we might associate with working life in a 'blame culture'. On the right-hand side we re-frame these three statements more appreciatively. We look at the same statement in a new way. See if you can complete the table. We can, of course, frame and re-frame in many ways. One big influence on how we frame things depends on our understanding of the context in which the statement was said.

As a mentor you may wish to devote some time, specifically, to encouraging your protégés to try to see things differently. This might be good news for at least two reasons. First, to encourage each protégé to tease out the positives from the present situation and to build on them. Second, because seeing things differently is the basic ingredient for being innovative. If we cannot see things in new and different ways, how can we ever be innovative in our practice?

We are suggesting that the ability to re-frame practice is a central process of reflective mentoring. Healthcare work is very value-laden so it is not surprising that we have different views on both practice and policy. Re-framing is a

Table 4.1.   Re-framing statements in an appreciative way

A statement	Framed one way	Re-framed appreciatively
1. 'You will do better next time'	Threat	Encouragement
2. 'I did not expect you to do it that way'	Reprimand	Concern
3. 'You need to take a break'	Order	Concern
4. 'I have not seen it being done like that'		
5. 'Well that is certainly a different approach to tackling the problem'		
6. 'Let's wait and see, shall we?'		
7. 'Why have you done it like that?'		
8. 'I know what to do'		
9. 'It would certainly help if you read up on that'		
10. Just watch me, I will show you'		

deliberately skilful way of turning things over and spinning them around, to see if they look any different, to look at a situation not just through our usual eyes, but through the eyes of others such as a patient, carer, doctor, social worker, probation officer and so on. It is about turning a downward spiral of digging deeper and deeper into problems, into a more virtuous and uplifting one focusing on successes.

3. Building a positive core of values and actions (practical wisdom)

Fulfilling this process is influenced by a protégé's success with the first two. What we know for sure is that building a positive core that is meaningful and useful will take time. Let us link this process with the previous purpose of reflective mentoring. Re-framing is not just about seeing things differently. It is also about choice. When we choose to pay attention to one aspect of a clinical encounter, to frame it in a particular way, for the time being, we are choosing to ignore other aspects of it. What we attend to is usually related to our values, in the sense that focusing on something implies that we value it. What we choose to ignore, is in some way, less important, less significant or less interesting right now. To enable protégés to build their positive cores, mentors might usefully invite them to talk about their values. It is our values that make us the kind of people we are. They also provide us with reasons why we do (or do not) act in particular ways. So they are very important things for protégés to come to know.

Reflective mentoring then involves engaging with a protégé in such a way that it helps them understand how their values affect their actions. It involves providing a context where they are able to appreciate how we need to try to align what we say about our practices (our espoused values) with what we actually do (our values in action).

In a recent large world-wide survey of employees, Rath (2007) found that only about a third of them could strongly agree with the following statement:

> *'At work, I have the opportunity to do what I do best every day'.*
>
> *Rath (2007, p. ii)*

Given how this connects with many aspects of what is called the 'psychological contract' we have with our employers (for example job satisfaction, going the extra step, voluntarily staying a bit later at work, putting that extra bit of effort into something, etc), it is clear that there is lots of room for organisations to benefit by improving the alignment between individual and collective strengths and jobs. Seligman (2002) argues that using strengths to better advantage:

> *'Makes work more fun, transforms a job or a career into a calling, increases flow...Moreover, by filling work with gratification, it is a long stride on the road to the good life'.*
>
> *Seligman (2002, p. 184)*

In a conversation with a protégé, a mentor might use the following questions to help build the protégés positive core of actions and values:

- What were you doing recently, in managing your time, that enabled you to use your strengths?
- What actions were you taking when you were successful at prioritising those things that you are really good at doing?
- What was happening when you found yourself thinking, 'that really worked well?
- What did someone say, or do, to make you feel that your professional experience was greatly appreciated?

- What strengths do you feel you have to 'fight fires' at work? (fire-fighting is about constantly fixing problems and dealing with what is urgent rather than what might be important). Maybe in fire-fighting the protégé is doing exactly what their strengths suit them for!
- What did you do that prompted your patient to say: *'Thank you, that feels much better'*?
- What were you doing that prompted a colleague to say: *'It is great working here'*?
- What did you say to a patient or colleague that enabled them to say: *'Thank you for understanding my situation'*?

All of these questions might be followed-up with: *'What do your answers tell you about those things you really value (your values) and the positive actions you can take to put your values into practice*?

4. Achieve and move forward

This is the fourth process of reflective mentoring. We suggest that mentoring is a means to an end. Primarily it is about enabling the protégé to do or achieve something different, more or even better with their positive core of values and actions. In other words, it is putting this core to good use to sustain and even amplify those aspects of their work that are proving to be nourishing and professionally successful. The previous process is essentially about articulating and deepening the protégé's understanding of what they feel is important in their work and why. In other words what they value. This fourth process is about *'what they actually do'*. For some, there is an important distinction to be made between envisioning a 'better' future situation, and actually being able to achieve this desired state. The challenge is not simply 'dreaming' of improving our practice and the clinical contexts in which it is embedded, but how to make this 'dream' a reality. In our view of reflective mentoring we are trying to emphasise that teasing out what is positive, within the present, and then working out ways to amplify this (the actions to take) is a key skill set that both the protégé and mentor need to have.

The 'dream' is not kindled by the protégé and mentor spending all their precious time searching for or talking about what is wrong, disappointing or unsatisfactory in the protégés practice. Future action needs to be inspired by those things that both parties feel are worth valuing, worth celebrating and sustaining. This might, in some cases, require some imagination. Protégé and mentor might have to discuss what the protégés practice might look like and what the team, unit, ward or organization could look like, if practice (and policy) were fully aligned around individual strengths and collective aspirations. One outcome of engaging in this fourth process is that each meeting, between protégé and mentor, is rounded off at least by some agreed 'statement of intent'. The content of this should include the grounded examples of the protégé's successful practice combined with aspects of the organisation's positive past. This statement captures the best of what is and links it purposefully with aspirations of what is to come.

Maybe the toughest part of reflective mentoring is simply letting go of negative stories of practice and working with the power of the protégés positive core of values and actions. To do this, the reflective mentor needs to skilfully use their appreciative intelligence.

References

Cooperrider D, Whitney D (2005) *Appreciative Inquiry: A Positive Revolution in Change.* Berrett-Koehler Publishers Inc, San Francisco

Dewey J (1933) *How We Think: A Restatement of the Relation of Reflective Thinking to the Educative Process.* Heath & Company, Lexington, M.A

Gardner H (1993) *Frames of Mind: The Theory of Multiple Intelligences.* Basic Books, New York

Ghaye T (2008) *Building the Reflective Healthcare Organisation.* Blackwell Publishing, Oxford

Handy C (1999) *The New Alchemists.* Hutchinson

Kierein NM, Gold MA (2000) Pygmalion in work organizations: a meta-analysis. *Journal of Organizational Behaviour* **21**(8): 913-928

O'Dowd A (2006) A motivational scheme at a London hospital encourages nurses to be helpful and friendly to patients. *Nursing Times* **102**(45): 9

Orem SL, Binkert J, Clancy AL (2007) *Appreciative Coaching: A Positive Process for Change.* Jossey-Bass, San Francisco

Rath T (2007) *StrengthsFinder 2.0.* Gallup Press, New York

Schön D (1983) *The Reflective Practitioner: How professionals think in action.* Basic Books, New York

Seligman M (2002) *Authentic Happiness.* Free Press, New York

Sensky T (2002) Withdrawal of life sustaining treatment. *British Medical Journal* **325**: 175-176

Thatchenkery T, Metzker C (2006) *Appreciative Intelligence: Seeing the Mighty Oak in the Acorn.* Berrett-Koehler Publishers Inc, San Francisco

Vize R (2007) Winning over NHS staff could be Brown's first big challenge. *Health Services Journal*: 21st June, 2007, p. 14.

CHAPTER 5

Mentoring with your social intelligence

In *Chapter 4* we linked excellence in reflective mentoring with our capability to use our appreciative intelligence. In a nutshell, appreciative intelligence is about how far we are able to re-frame a given situation and, in doing so, recognise the positive possibilities embedded in it. It also involves action — the necessary action to positively engage with our protégés so that valued outcomes unfold from the generative aspects of the current mentoring situation. Appreciative intelligence is situated in the field of multiple intelligences, something proposed by Howard Gardner (1993). Gardner (1993) demonstrated that intelligence was not a single ability but a number of capacities. He based his view on findings from disciplines such as anthropology, psychology and cognitive science, and from the biographies of exceptional individuals.

Thatchenkery and Metzker (2006) argue that our appreciative intelligence is another type of intelligence within the multiple intelligence field. They propose that there are three components of appreciative intelligence: the ability to re-frame, appreciate the positive and see how the future unfolds from the present. For this to happen, they urge, we need to be persistent, have self-belief, have a tolerance for uncertainty and have irrepressible resilience. Because the people we interviewed could re-frame, appreciate the positive and see how the future could unfold from the present, they could see how their end goal was possible to accomplish. Thus, they were willing to persist and to believe that their own actions and abilities would take them to a successful conclusion. Because they could envision the way a positive future could unfold from the present, they could deal with the uncertainty that often accompanies a new venture or a crisis. They exhibited irrepressible resilience, the ability to bounce back from a difficult situation as the result of re-framing, seeing what was positive in the situation, and understanding that a better future could come about despite a crisis or setback (Thatchenkery and Metzker, 2006).

In this chapter we want to link reflective mentoring with the importance of using your social intelligence. In our view of reflective mentoring there is a focus on the 'we' (the mentor and protégé) and on the idea of a good working relationship between them. By implication, this requires mentors to draw upon their social intelligence

(Goleman, 2006). Central to this are the processes of collaborative working and appreciative knowledge sharing (Thatchenkery, 2005). These have at least two significant associated processes. For those involved, it is sensing how others feel, or knowing what they might think. Some call this empathy, or social awareness. The second associated process helps make the most of this awareness. It is about being able to use this sensing capability to interact with others (i.e. the protégé) positively. More specifically, we suggest that reflective mentoring requires the mentor to:

- **Have a sense of attunement**: The ability to pay attention to what their protégés are feeling, saying and doing. Listening to them and especially their point/s of view, even when these are different to your own.
- **Be aware of self-presentation**: For example, being able to behave in such a way that we do not alienate those we are mentoring. It is not about being loud, assertive, self-opinionated or controlling. It is about presenting ourselves in a way that invites protégés to understand 'where we are coming from' and why, when we say what we do and act in a certain manner.
- **Use the power to influence wisely**: A central tenet of reflective mentoring is that everyone involved has the right to influence the outcomes of particular mentoring sessions and produce a desired social result.
- **Have a sense of attachment and bonding**: For example, an ability and preparedness to build trust between those involved in the process, to be seen to be striving to meet particular, individual and group needs, to be kind towards and care for each other.

Reflective mentoring can be seen as a genuinely caring act that has the potential to promote the health and wellbeing of others. It is not only about our relationships with our protégés, but also how we act in them. Put another way, it is not only about roles and responsibilities (see *Chapter 3*), but also about our ability to act wisely and appreciatively when in the company of our protégés. This makes reflective mentoring a highly skilful social action that requires positive connection, mutual attention and empathy. It is a skilfulness underpinned by our capability to use both our appreciative and social intelligences. This is challenging and illustrated below.

Tough love and tough bugs

An NHS hospital asked us to give them some advice about how to improve their multi-disciplinary peer group mentoring process. After a honeymoon period, which lasted for about six months, attendance had begun to drop off and there were 'murmurings' that staff were not getting as much out of the process as they had hoped. We sat in on one of their monthly meetings. What follows is a reconstruction of one set of verbal exchanges between some of those (eight staff and a mentor) who attended. The focus for the session was the trust's plan to get going with their cleaner hospital programme. A 'problem' for the hospital was that being too busy on the wards was stopping staff attending any kind of training on infection control. Solving this problem was seen as a trust priority. The group thought it was something significant for them to discuss. As a hospital-wide concern, this 'problem' was essentially located outside the group. Through their peer mentoring session, there was a hope that a solution might come from within the group. What follows captures the 'mood' on the day:

Jane: *'I try to share my ideas about solving this but sometimes I feel, well, they fall on deaf ears. This makes me feel invisible...ignored and well...well unappreciated'*

Jo: *'Oh no, no Jane. No. This is not right. We do listen. I think we should discuss this'*

[Four other staff members say at the same time]: *'Yes we do, we do. Oh Jane no'*

Jane: *'I think it's very important that we use this time to discuss our ideas. I try to explain my feelings about this and I think you* [pointing at the mentor] *can encourage everyone to do the same'*

Cynthia: *'When we meet to solve problems like this, it usually generates lots of new ideas from team members here. This is what it should be. But the problem, as I see it anyway, is that often these ideas aren't developed. We tend to fly around. One idea doesn't get connected to the previous one!* [an embarrassing chuckle goes around the group like a Mexican wave]

Sarah (the mentor): *'I think you're being a bit hard on yourselves. My role, as you know, is to bring ideas, based on my experience, to this group. I hope this will trigger new ideas from you'*

Cynthia: *'Sometimes I feel that a danger for us is to come up with too many ideas!* [more laughter]. *We have to try to sort through the different ideas because we all have different opinions and solutions...and backgrounds. You* [pointing to a couple of colleagues] *always seem to see things from a patient experience view. Of course...and that's why we are here. We don't want to cause any unnecessary pain or anxiety. They're our "customers", to use this new term. They've got to be confident in what we do. I know you* [Sam] *see infection control as affecting bed availability and the nightmares you have. Like the example you told me about last week, remember? About patients waiting for hip replacement surgery and there's a patient with an infection and they occupy that bed three times as long as they should have. And there's two other patients who would have had their surgery had that bed not been occupied. It's not right'*

Jo: *'Jane you are the creative one. What do you think we need to do?'*

Jane: *'Yes, but you* [pointing to three nurses who had known each other for 16 years] *understand each other. I'm not sure we understand each other'*

Jo: *'No I don't think you're right. We do listen to each other. Don't we?* [a silence]. *Do you feel we don't understand you?* [increasingly anxious looks buzz around the group]'

Jane: *'Well sometimes I think, whatever I say doesn't matter. I think everyone agrees it's the right thing to do...control infections. It's obvious. We need to be creative so that we can train more staff in infection control. The problem is there's a right way to do it and a wrong way to do it. And we need to make sure we do this the right way'*

Jo: *'Agreed. We are not disagreeing with you. What we need to do is plan how we can get the message across to all staff about how to stop infections from happening rather than treating them after they occur'*

Sarah: *'For example, how good are we at washing our hands between seeing patients? Is there any excuse for poor hand washing? We've got scope to do a lot more than this. So what shall we do?'*

Cynthia: *'I think we should plan a training programme around best practice'*

Jo: *'Well around basic hygiene'*

Bronwen: *'Hospital cleanliness, which are the dirty wards?* [some laughter]. *The doctors are the worst culprits!'*

Sam: *'But we've got to make sure staff know what they can do to help'*

Cynthia: *'Yes. This will be good because Freda* [from the hospital's PALS Service] *tells me that she is getting more and more complaints about some of the toilet facilities over there'*

Jane: *'Has anyone heard of the government's "Saving Lives Toolkit" and its five high impact interventions?'*

Faith: '*We could get marketing to do something on superbugs [laughter]*'

Bronwen: '*We need a strategy*'.

There was a lot going on in this meeting. There was much (for all) to learn from reflecting on the nature of these exchanges. Sarah (the mentor) felt that what went on was fairly typical. She described this session as 'full of energy'. She also felt somewhat frustrated at times by the way some of the group spoke to each other. She felt they said one thing to each other, but then did something else which contradicted this. She asked us the direct question: '*Do you think, as their mentor, that they need me to give them some tough love? To steer and direct them more?*'. For those unfamiliar with this expression, tough love is often used when someone treats another person assertively, even harshly or sternly, in order to help them in the long run. One concern about tough love is that it assumes that such (tough) behaviours produce positive outcomes. Tough love from a mentor links with the issues of over and under-responsibility.

Consider the following:

- Who was learning what during this meeting?
- Who and what was being appreciated?
- Who was doing any kind of re-framing? What was being re-framed and looked at in different ways?
- What kinds of core values and actions were emerging from the discussion?
- What had been achieved and how far, do you think, the staff involved felt that they were moving forward?

One interpretation of these verbal exchanges is that they are very much focused on solving a 'problem' — a large hospital-wide one. While there seems to be no shortage of ideas, what does appear to be missing is any appreciation of what is currently working well, throughout the hospital, with regard to healthcare-associated infection, and how future action might build on this success.

Reflective mentoring brought into wholeness

With the aim that reflective mentoring does not become an endless list of mentor attributes and processes we try, in *Figure 5.1*, to bring what we have said so far in the book into some kind of wholeness. *Figure 5.1* is not a 'model'. It is a framework for understanding what is involved in being a reflective mentor.

The notion of appreciative lenses links with the use of our appreciative intelligence and refers to different ways of looking, listening and learning from the protégé. We are never free of lenses. They help us apprehend the world

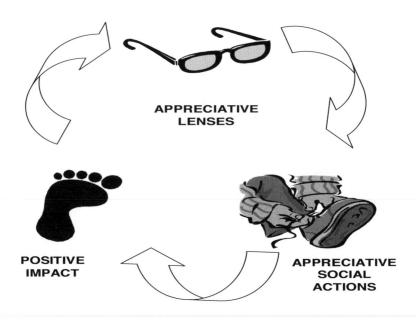

APPRECIATIVE
LENSES

POSITIVE
IMPACT

APPRECIATIVE
SOCIAL
ACTIONS

Figure 5.1 Appreciative lenses that are useful in reflective mentoring.

around us. Each of the lenses we describe helps the mentor perceive in a certain way. Peshkin (2001) used the phrase *'angles of vision'* to capture the idea of consciously using different lenses to expand and enrich our ways of seeing and making sense of our interactions with others. We use the word lenses because they also provide a means of 'looking into' something. For example, something significant that the protégé has brought to the mentoring session. Using these appreciative lenses is an attention-focusing process. In *Table 5.1* we describe five different, but complementary, appreciative lenses that are useful in reflective mentoring.

Appreciative social actions (see *Table 5.2*) links with the way we use our social intelligence. They refer to the different kinds of action, or steps taken, by those involved in the mentoring process. Again we suggest five different kinds of appreciative social actions that are useful.

Positive impact (see *Table 5.3*) refers to achievements. The metaphor of a footprint is used to symbolise what the mentoring process has accomplished to date. What it has 'left behind'. Its mark on the lived experiences of the protégé and significant others involved (for example patients, colleagues). The notion of

Table 5.1.   Some appreciative lenses used by reflective mentors

Kinds of lens	Some reflective questions
Communication lens	*What is the protégé essentially trying to say, and how?*
Values lens	*What is your view on what your protégé is saying?*
Participation lens	*Who was/is involved in what your protégé is describing?*
Time lens	*What happened earlier in the protégé's description that helps you grasp the meaning of what is happening now?*
Pattern lens	*How far is your protégé talking about something that occurs regularly, routinely, occasionally or under certain circumstances?*

Table 5.2.   Some appreciative social actions (steps) taken by reflective mentors

Kinds of step	Some reflective questions
Contemplative step	*What is the protégé committed to doing?*
Supported step	*What is/are the most appropriate ways to support your protégé?*
First step	*What did you decide to do as a priority with your protégé?*
Political step	*Who benefits from the steps taken?*
Dance step	*How do you plan to keep things moving in the direction agreed between you and your protégé?*

Table 5.3. **Some positive impact (footprints) that arise from the reflective mentoring process**

Kinds if footprint	Some reflective questions
Learning print	*What are the main things you have learnt in achieving particular dance steps?*
Complex print	*How far is there an alignment between your protégé's values and their actions?*
Unique print	*How far has the mentoring process provided an opportunity to be creative in achieving an agreed goal?*
Ethos print	*In what way/s has the mentoring process affected the protégé's view of what it is like to work in their organization*
Future print	*In what ways can the protégé's future footprint/s be positively influenced by their current achievements?*

'leaving footprints' is significant in terms of feeling a sense of achievement and progress. Footprints mark the course of travel, the experiential journey for both protégé and mentor. It is a trail of where we have come from. It is 'how we have got here, from where we were'. Therefore footprint-type evidence is important to think about. In its very minimal form it might be a brief note/summary of what was discussed and agreed at each mentoring meeting. The idea of 'footprints' may also generate a sense of realistic optimism amongst those involved, about future possibilities, and a feel for what is achievable.

References

Peshkin A (2001) Angles of Vision: Enhancing perception in qualitative research. *Qualitative Inquiry* **7**: 238- 253

Gardner H (1993) *Frames of Mind: The Theory of Multiple Intelligences*, Fontana Press, London

Thatchenkery T, Metzker C (2006) *Appreciative Intelligence: Seeing the Mighty Oak in the Acorn.* Berrett-Koehler Publishers Inc, San Francisco.

Goleman D (2006) *Social Intelligence: The New Science of Social Relationships.* Bantam Books.

Thatchenkery T (2005) *Appreciative Sharing of Knowledge: Leveraging Knowledge Management for Strategic Change.* Taos Institute Publication, Chagrin Falls

Conclusion

In this book we have tried to 'position' reflective mentoring within the field of reflective learning and link it to a number of more appreciative processes for improving the way we mentor our protégés. We suggest that at the heart of reflective mentoring is a conversation. Throughout the book we have tried to show that effective reflective mentoring is achieved through a conversation where the mentor tries to:

● Enable their protégés to move away from any pre-occupation with 'problems', which can easily turn into deficit-based conversations, and toward achievements. These conversations are more strengths-based and can be uplifting. Reflective mentoring, as we have described it, is not just about solving problems and addressing suffering, it is also about celebrating achievements and discovering something new.

● Help their protégés to see their practice, and maybe what goes on in their work environment/s, differently and in new ways. This can be a very hard thing to do, especially if the protégé has been used to seeing an aspect of their work in one way for a long time. Seeing things differently can open up new ways of doing things. We have called this a process of re-framing.

● Work supportively with their protégés to build a positive core of values that each protégé feels they can put into action. These values make us the kind of people we are. They represent what we stand for and provide us with the reasons for doing what we do. They re-connect us with the central purposes about why we work in healthcare. They are the basis of our practical wisdom.

● Enable their protégés to feel a sense of achievement in their work and to move forward by amplifying those aspects of their practice that are particularly successful and significant to each of them. Through conversation, the reflective mentor may have to encourage each protégé to understand the distinction between longer and shorter-term achievements. Achievements can also be thought of in terms of results and in terms of effects. Results can be thought of as relatively concrete and visible achievements. They usually stem from implementing an action plan, from a new routine, from attending a training day and so on. Results are linked with goal fulfilment. Effects may be more subtle and subjective achievements. For example, as a consequence of engaging with their mentor, the protégé may feel that the process has made them more self-confident, more motivated, have a greater capacity for work and so on.

What we are saying about reflective mentoring through conversation may not be remarkable or unique. However having said this, what we believe to be very challenging is finding a process that works for BOTH the protégé and the mentor. The process of reflective mentoring we describe can help all concerned move from joint discussion, to shared learning and on to positive action. It can help the protégé commit to the short term application of something and also to appreciate the longer term implications of this.

Reflective mentoring and the generation of practical knowledge

Reflective mentoring through conversation is about a way of interacting and asking questions, of positively responding to them and making sense of practice. The aim of the conversation is to enable the protégé to feel a real sense of achievement and move their practice forward. The conversation between the mentor and protégé is therefore a process of knowledge generation and appreciative knowledge sharing. Fundamentally, it is about trying to reveal what we know, how we know what we know, and what constitutes really practical and useful knowledge? In addition to these questions, we can add two more action-oriented ones. Namely, what can we do with the knowledge that springs from the reflective mentoring process, and how can better practices be sustained? So with action must come commitment. The full skilfulness of the reflective mentor is needed to address the danger of the protégé going backwards, of falling into depression and disillusionment as 'reality' is revealed through the conversation process. As we have said, this process is one that needs to be conducted ethically as the protégé may well be thinking:

- What do you (the mentor) want me to say?
- What do I have the courage to say?
- How much do I expose?
- Do I fear a loss of control?

The challenge of reflective mentoring is to try to keep the protégé focused on working towards better practices and better working conditions, on deepening their understanding of what *is* working well and why, and then amplifying it. This requires a shared sense of hopefulness and a curiosity to find out, and work out, what might be done more or better in caring practice. Curiosity is the imagination in action. The reflective mentor needs to cultivate a protégé's curiosity, their ability to learn to dance with ideas in their heads amidst the nitty-gritty of everyday practice. Perhaps this is something for further reflection?

Index

A

Achievement 42
Active listening 30
Appreciations 71
Appreciative gaze 42
Appreciative intelligence 67–76
Appreciative lenses 82
Approachable 53
Assessor 17, 56
Attunement 78

B

Befriending 52
Benefits 60
Bonding 78
Buddy 19

C

Care 23
Career counsellor 53
Challenger 54
Clinical. *See also* Supervisor
Coach 19
Committed 53
Communication 22
Communicator 53
Competence 57
Conceptions 11–28
Constructionist perspective 34
Conversation 33–47
Coordinator 19
Core values 73
Counsellor 19

Critical friend 19
Critical thinker 55

D

Definition 49
Diagrams. *See also* Conversations
Door-opener 56

E

Education. *See also* Professional groups
Environment 20
Envisioner 58
Expectations 68
Eye-opener 55

F

Facilitator 19
Feedback-giver 56
Footprints 84

G

Galatea effect 68
Golem effect 69

H

Healthcare. *See also* Professional groups